Name _____

▶ **Directions**

Read the following story. Circle each word that has the /k/ sound.

...usually stand for the /k/ sound.

king   ti**ck**le   opa**que**

The Shaggy Bird

The kiwi is a stocky, tailless bird about the size of a chicken. It has shaggy feathers that look like hair. Its wings are small and it cannot fly. Its beak is long, with nostrils at the tip. It has a keen sense of smell, which helps it find food. This makes the kiwi unique, because most birds have a poor sense of smell.

If you would like to visit this bird, seek it in the thick, wet forests of New Zealand. Keep your eyes open and walk quietly, though. These birds are afraid of people.

▶ **Directions**

Write a word from the box to complete each sentence.

Rule When the letters **qu** appear at the beginning of a word, they usually stand for the /kw/ sound.

queen   **qu**iet   **qu**iz

questioned	quake	quite	quarter	quick

1. Carla's legs began to _____ as she heard "On your mark!"

2. Carla was as _____ as a deer, but so was her rival Jenny.

3. Last month, she _____ whether she should enter this race.

4. However, Carla's coach said he was _____ sure she was ready.

5. She grasped her lucky _____ as the starter yelled, "Go!"

► **Directions**

Circle each word containing **ch** in the following sentences. Then write each circled word in the correct column below the sentences.

Rule The letters **ch** usually stand for the sound at the beginning and end of **church**. Sometimes the letters **ch** can stand for the /k/ or the /sh/ sound.

chorus   chivalry

1. Charlotte's party began right on schedule.
2. Charles led a small orchestra in playing "Happy Birthday."
3. Charlotte's favorite present was a chemistry set.
4. She also liked the silver chain and silver charm bracelet.
5. The new student came in a chauffeur-driven car.
6. Carrie brought some chopped chives and bean dip.
7. A special chef made chocolate cake.
8. Our stomachs ached, but we played charades anyway.

/k/	/ch/	/sh/

► **Directions**

Circle each word in which the letters **kn** stand for the **n** sound.

Rule The letters **kn** usually stand for the /n/ sound in **knee**. The letter **k** is silent.

9. Sandy has always had a knack for camping.
10. He packs his knapsack carefully.
11. First he puts his scout knife into the flap.
12. Next he folds his knitted cap and gloves.
13. When everything is packed, he ties a secure knot.

Name _____

▶ **Directions**

Underline each word in the sentences that contains the letter **c**. Then write /k/ or /s/ above each **c** to show which sound it stands for.

Rule When the letter **c** comes before **a, o,** or **u,** it usually stands for the /k/ sound. When **c** comes before **e, i,** or **y,** it usually stands for the /s/ sound.

coat   silence

1. For centuries, people have wanted to comprehend outer space.

2. A Russian satellite named *Sputnik I* circled the earth in 1957.

3. This was a major advance in the conquest of space.

4. The first person to travel into space was cosmonaut Yuri Gagarin.

5. In 1969, the world celebrated when U.S astronauts Armstrong and Aldrin landed on the moon.

6. Today, space shuttles take off from the Kennedy Space Center in Florida.

7. There, audiences anticipate the countdown as spacecraft are sent into space.

8. In the cabin, astronauts rely on computers to control the blastoff.

9. During a mission, astronauts carry out many complicated procedures and experiments.

10. People seem to welcome the excitement of facing the unknown.

Directions

Read each word below. Write /g/ in the blank if the word has the hard **g** sound. Write /j/ if the word contains the **j** sound.

Rule The letters **g** and **dge** can stand for the /j/ sound. Sometimes the letter **g** stands for the hard /g/ sound.

page   bri**dge**   **g**ate

1. region _____
2. gentle _____
3. giant _____
4. stage _____
5. endangered _____
6. gobbled _____
7. largest _____
8. gorillas _____
9. range _____
10. disgust _____
11. edge _____
12. pledge _____

Directions

Write the word from the list above that completes each sentence. Use each word only once.

13. We met on the school _____ to build the set for the play.

14. Our play is about saving the wild _____.

15. Gorillas are the _____ of all the apes.

16. They look a bit scary, but actually they are quite _____.

17. These _____ apes live in groups of 30 animals or more.

18. Each group has a territory that will _____ from 5 to 15 miles.

19. We decided to make the stage look like a _____ of the rain forest where the gorillas live.

20. Gorillas are _____, mostly because people are cutting down the rain forests.

21. We soon stopped for lunch, but Harry had _____ all the sandwiches.

22. "Act your age," snapped Marla in _____.

23. After working hard, we sat on the

_____ of the stage and rested.

24. We decided to _____ some of the money from the play to a wildlife fund.

Name _____

▶ Directions

Read the words in the box. Then read the story. Write the correct word from the box to complete each unfinished sentence.

protective	goal	chorus	stocky	century	cheers
back	tackling	protect	because	block	quicker

Football and Safety

The team with the ball lines up to form a *T.* The quarterback drops _____

and gives the ball to the fullback. As his players _____ for him, the

_____ fullback carries the football across the _____

line. Touchdown! There is a _____ of _____ from the

fans.

Did you every wonder how football began? Some people think the game got started in the

middle of the last _____. Back then, there were no

_____ uniforms or helmets. None were needed

_____ the game was very similar to soccer.

Over the years, football players gradually increased the amount of running, blocking, and

_____. To accomplish this, players had to become _____

and stronger. Even so, football players were often injured. Helmets, pads, and uniforms were

developed to better _____ the players.

Read each numbered word. Write the letter of the word or word group that has the same meaning. Then read the story and paraphrase it, changing each word or word group in boldface print. Use the words in the list to help you.

Hint There is usually more than one way to express an idea. When you **paraphrase** something, you use different words to give the same meaning.

_____ **1.** unique

_____ **2.** clever

_____ **3.** became

_____ **4.** gained

_____ **5.** occasionally

_____ **6.** conceived

_____ **7.** peculiar

_____ **8.** commonly

a. one-of-a-kind

b. strange

c. was

d. once in a while

e. invented

f. regularly

g. won

h. smart

Chess Greats

Chess is a **one-of-a-kind** game. The idea for chess was probably **invented** in India about 1,500 years ago. Through the years, there have been some imaginative and **smart** players.

For example, in the early 1900s, Harry Nelson Pillsbury got into a **strange** habit. He **regularly** played 12 to 16 chess games at once—while blindfolded.

Once in a while people became skillful chess players at a very early age. Samuel Reshevsky **was** a chess master at age eight. Bobby Fischer **won** the U.S. chess title in 1958 at age fourteen.

_____

_____

_____

_____

_____

_____

_____

_____

Name _____

▶ **Directions**

Circle the correct word to complete each analogy. Then draw a box around the letter or letters that stand for the /f/ sound in each underlined word.

Rule The letters **f, ff,** or **ph** usually stand for the /f/ sound.
fish   ta**ff**y   tele**ph**one

Definition An **analogy** compares different things. Analogies show how pairs of things are alike.

A **car** is to a **road** as a **boat** is to **water.**

(A car travels over a road, and a boat travels over water.)

1. **L e a f** is to **tree** as **f e a t h e r** is to
   cabin.   snake.   bird.

2. **Sea** is to **f i s h i n g** as **f i e l d** is to
   calling.   farming.   swimming.

3. **Last** is to **f i n a l** as **p h o n y** is to
   fake.   end.   phone.

4. **Neck** is to **g i r a f f e** as **trunk** is to
   robin.   pack.   elephant.

5. **T e l e p h o n e** is to **talking** as **p a m p h l e t**
   is to speaking.   reading.   phoning.

6. **F e e t** is to **f o o t** as **f i n g e r s** is to
   toe.   finger.   fine.

7. **P h a n t o m** is to **ghost** as **end** is to
   start.   elf.   finish.

8. **Camera** is to **p h o t o** as **tape recorder** is to
   walls.   picture.   recording.

9. **Baker** is to **f l o u r** as **f l o r i s t** is to
   flowers.   floors.   glasses.

10. **Niece** is to **n e p h e w** as **aunt** is to
    fly.   uncle.   lion.

11. **P h y s i c i a n** is to **body** as **dentist** is to
    hair.   nails.   teeth.

12. **Sentence** is to **p a r a g r a p h** as **word** is to
    sentence.   letter.   sound.

▶ **Directions**

Read each sentence and underline the word or words containing **gh**. Then write each **gh** word in the correct column at the bottom to show which sound, if any, it stands for.

Rule The letters **gh** can stand for the /g/ sound or the /f/ sound. Sometimes **gh** is silent and stands for no sound.

ghost   lau**gh**   naug**h**ty

1. I hoped we would have enough food for our community party.
2. I sighed as I realized I had practically bought out the grocery store.
3. I had gotten bread and rolls, olives, and gherkin pickles.
4. I had gotten lean meat so it wouldn't be tough.
5. Some of the neighbors were making salads and desserts.
6. I thought about the terrible party we had during a blizzard last year.
7. It was a ghastly day.
8. Everyone had a rough time getting to our house.
9. The snow-covered guests arrived looking like ghosts.
10. It seemed that everyone was coughing and sneezing.
11. The howling wind made a ghostly sound in the chimney.
12. Afterward, everyone laughed about it.

/f/	/g/	no sound
_____	_____	_____
_____	_____	_____
_____	_____	_____
_____	_____	_____
_____		

Name _____

▶ **Directions**

Write each word in the box on the line beside its definition. Then write /s/, /z/, /sh/, or /zh/ to show the sound that **s** stands for in that word.

Rule The letter **s** usually stands for the /s/ sound you hear at the beginning of **silent**. Sometimes the letter **s** can stand for the /z/, /sh/, or /zh/ sound.

easy   sugar   treasure

noisy	miser	similar	usual	harvest	insurance
reservoir	hasten	result	measure	leisure	research

1. _____ ____ free time

2. _____ ____ a place that holds an extra, or reserve, supply; often a lake where water is collected

3. _____ ____ careful investigation of something

4. _____ ____ ordinary or customary

5. _____ ____ full of loud and usually unpleasant sounds

6. _____ ____ find the size or amount of something

7. _____ ____ almost, but not exactly, the same

8. _____ ____ a greedy or stingy person who doesn't want to spend money

9. _____ ____ a contract that pays money to a person if, for example, something the person owns is stolen

10. _____ ____ gathering of a crop

11. _____ ____ to speed up; to move or act swiftly

12. _____ ____ what happens because of something; the outcome

The sentences in the paragraphs below include words that contain the letter **s**. The sentences are not in the correct order. Number the sentences within each group to show the correct order. Then underline each letter **s** that stands for the /s/ sound and circle each letter **s** that stands for the /z/ sound.

1.

_____ This is because Sally enjoys making others laugh.

_____ However, her sad mood doesn't often last long.

_____ Sometimes Sally Simpson feels unhappy.

_____ Here is what happens: Sally puts a plastic crimson rose between her teeth and vigorously hums a song.

_____ When other people are happy, then suddenly Sally isn't sad any more.

2.

_____ The combination of drums, saxophone, and horns was too much.

_____ After two "For Sale" signs appeared overnight, my parents suggested that we play one of their favorite songs—"Far, Far Away."

_____ I've always loved music, so one day I decided to compose some songs.

_____ When I succeeded in writing several pieces, I invited my friends Sally, Susan, and Sam over to play them.

 Directions

Choose four words containing the letter **s** from the sentences above and use them in original sentences of your own.

_____

_____

_____

_____

Name _____

▶ **Directions**

Use a word from the box to complete each sentence. Then write /h/ or /hw/ on the line at the right to show which sound the word contains.

Rule The letters **wh** can stand for the **h** sound or the **hw** sound.
who   what

where	wheelchair	what	whiskers
whiff	whole	whistle	whale
wheat	when	whisked	whispered

1. Sue and Al didn't know what to buy _____ they got to the store. _____

2. "_____ should we get for Stu's birthday?" asked Al. _____

3. "How about a _____ to call his new dog!" _____

4. "_____ are the pet supplies?" asked Al. _____

5. "The _____ area at the back of the store is for pets," said the salesman. _____

6. "Get a _____ of that perfume," gagged Sue. _____

7. "Don't insult the people who like it," _____ Al. _____

8. Sue and Al _____ through the store quickly and left. _____

▶ **Directions**

Choose the word from the box above which matches each meaning below. Write each word on the line in front of its definition.

9. _____ a beard

10. _____ a chair which can move from place to place on wheels

11. _____ a huge animal that lives in the ocean

12. _____ a grain used to make flour

▶ **Directions**

Read each word in the box. Then write it on the line beside its definition.

Rule The letters **sh, ci, ce,** and **ti** can stand for the /sh/ sound.
polish   ocean
social   patience

| special | fashion | Oceania | election |

1. _____ popular or up-to-date style

2. _____ the process of voting for candidates or issues

3. _____ the lands of the central and south Pacific

4. _____ distinctive, unusual, or unique

▶ **Directions**

As you read the story, circle each word that has the /sh/ sound. Then write the words you circled in the correct columns below. Write each word only once.

Learning About Oceans

Since the days of the ancient Greeks and Phoenicians, people have been interested in exploring the vast oceans that surround us. For a long time people have been fed by the wide variety of fish, mammals, and crustaceans that inhabit the waters of the earth.

Through patient exploration, we have learned basic information about the oceans, but there is much left to find out. The study of the sea is called oceanography, and the scientists who study it are called oceanographers. These scientists spend some of their time working on research ships. They study many different things. Some study waves and tides. Some study how the ocean floor is shaped and how shores are formed. Others study the living creatures of the sea. Some scientists have found offshore oil deposits with the potential to help us maintain a sufficient supply of fuel.

ce	ti	sh	ci
_____	_____	_____	_____
_____	_____	_____	_____
_____	_____	_____	_____
_____	_____	_____	_____
	_____		

Name _____

▶ **Directions**

Read the article. Then circle the letter of the correct answer for each question.

Telephone Features

The first telephone system was not very efficient. Only four people used the same line. No one had a telephone number. People called each other by pushing a knob on the phone.

Over the years, people sought ways to improve the telephone system. Telephones today are a triumph of modern technology. People all over the world can talk to each other.

Some phone features are surprising. For example, if you get a feature called "call forwarding" on your phone, you can dial a code to tell your home telephone where you will be. If someone dials your number, the telephone will ring where you are instead of at your home.

Another bright telephone idea is "automatic callback." With this feature, you can reach a person whose line is busy as soon as he or she hangs up. Your telephone will call you and connect you with the other person when he or she gets off the line.

What will telephones be like in the future? Will people be able to see the person they are talking to? We only know that the phones of the future will be improved in ways that we cannot imagine today.

1. The first telephone system was not **efficient.** What does **efficient** mean?
   a. having color   b. modern-looking
   c. able to be used without wasting time

2. Telephones are a **triumph** of modern technology. What does **triumph** mean?
   a. oddity   b. success   c. sad ending

3. Over the years, people **sought** ways to improve the telephone system. What does **sought** mean?
   a. looked for   b. forgot about
   c. did not want

4. Another **bright** telephone idea is called "automatic callback." What does **bright** mean in this sentence?
   a. giving much light   b. lively and peppy
   c. clever and helpful

5. The phone **system** of tomorrow will have many additional improvements. What is a **system?**
   a. a map or graph   b. a set of parts that form a whole
   c. showing how something is taken apart

Carefully read the paragraph below. Pay attention to the main ideas.

Hint When you paraphrase information, you put it into your own words. In order to paraphrase, you need to understand the most important ideas.

Telephone Etiquette

Telephone etiquette is easy to learn. Suppose you want to call Ricardo, the neighbor next door. First find the phone number for Ricardo in the white pages of the phone book. When you have found the number, dial it with patience and care and allow time for Ricardo to answer. When Ricardo answers, identify yourself and tell Ricardo why you are calling. Keep your message brief, because someone else may want to use the telephone. These simple suggestions can make using the phone a pleasure for you, your family, your neighbors, and your friends.

Directions

Paraphrase the paragraph above by writing three sentences that give the same information as the long paragraph. On the lines below, write a sentence for each step to follow for placing a telephone call.

Telephone Etiquette

_____

_____

_____

_____

_____

_____

_____

_____

Name _____

 Directions

The sentences in the paragraphs below include words that contain the letters **th**. The sentences are not in the correct order. First number the sentences in each group to show the correct order. Then underline each **th** as in **thin** and circle each **th** as in **then**.

Rule The letters **th** can stand for the /th/ sound as in **thin**. The letters **th** can also stand for the /th/ sound as in **then**.

1.

_____ Then Mother heard that running is healthful, so she and I joined in.

_____ Father really started something when he began to run.

_____ First, my brother Matthew began to run with Dad.

_____ Now my whole family is so enthusiastic about running that we will enter a marathon on Thursday.

2.

_____ "I'd rather go out myself," thought Kim, but she thawed a thick pizza to eat.

_____ Mom asked Kim to baby-sit for her baby brother while her parents went to the theater.

_____ "Thank you a thousand times, Kim," said her mother when they returned. "You're a faithful sister."

_____ Later she threw a ball for her brother Seth, who got enthusiastic each time the ball went farther.

 Directions

Choose two words containing the letters **th** from the sentences above and use them in original sentences of your own.

_____

_____

_____

Directions

Underline each word in which you see the letters **sc**. Then write /sk/, /s/, or /sh/ above each word you underlined to show the sound that **sc** stands for in that word.

Rule The letters **sc** can stand for the /sk/, /s/, or /sh/ sounds.
scalp   scientist
conscience

1. At the art museum, we scanned the landscapes first.

2. In one scene, a farmer held a huge scythe.

3. Another painting showed a luscious scarlet sunset.

4. In one room we were conscious of the scent of paint.

5. A man on a tall scaffold scowled at us.

6. Throughout our visit, Amy took conscientious notes.

7. I paid scant attention to the paintings about wars.

8. Many scenes in the modern art section seemed straight from science fiction.

9. I scampered into the sculpture room to see if they had any work by the sculptor Michelangelo.

Directions

Choose a word from those you underlined above to fit each definition.

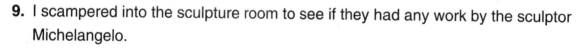

_____ showing care

_____ glanced at or looked over

_____ moved quickly

_____ smell

_____ pictures of natural inland scenery

_____ frowned

Name _____

▶ **Directions**

Read the words in the box. Underline each word that contains the letters **gn** and circle each word that contains the letters **tch.** Then use the words to complete the sentences below.

Rule The letters **gn** can stand for the /n/ sound. The letters **tch** can stand for the /ch/ sound.

gnat   si**gn**   ma**tch**   ki**tch**en

resign	watch	stitching	batches	kitchen
assign	catching	design	pitchers	campaign

My aunt was in charge of the mayor's reelection _____ . She had

to _____ tasks to the other volunteers. She asked people to bake

_____ of cookies and make _____ of iced tea for

neighborhood meetings. She found an artist to _____ election posters.

My cousin helped by _____ a banner to hang in the center of town.

It was a difficult campaign. One candidate was demanding that the mayor

_____ before the election!

My aunt kept a close _____ on the election polls. At first the mayor

seemed to have a good lead. Then the polls showed that another candidate was

_____ up. In the end, however, the mayor won the election. And my aunt

had run the whole campaign from her _____ .

Directions

Write each word from the box beside its definition.

Rule The letters **rh** and **wr** can stand for the /r/ sound.
rhythm
wreath

Rhine	wreck	rhubarb	wrath	wrap
playwright	wring	rhyme	rhinoceros	wrist

1. a great anger _____

2. the part of the body between the hand and arm _____

3. to squeeze or twist _____

4. a person who writes plays _____

5. ruin of a ship, car, or other vehicle _____

6. having the same sound at the end of words or verses _____

7. river flowing from Switzerland through Germany, and into the North Sea _____

8. huge animal with one or two horns on its nose that is found in Africa and Asia _____

9. plant with thick stalks that can be cooked or baked _____

10. to cover with something _____

Directions

Complete each sentence by choosing the correct word from the box above.

11. The _____ has written many plays about her adventures.

12. One play is set on the _____ River in Germany.

13. In another, she describes the _____ of a famous steamship.

14. Three of the plays are written in _____ rather than prose.

15. Toward critics, she feels nothing but _____ .

16. "I'd like to _____ his neck," she said of one critic.

Name _____

Directions

Write **ear, pear,** or **pearl** to show which sound the letters **ear** stand for.

Rule The letters **ear** can stand for the /ear/ sound, the /air/ sound, or the /ur/ sound.
app**ear** /ear/   p**ear** /air/
p**earl** /ur/

1. weary _____
2. earnest _____
3. spear _____
4. earth _____
5. tear _____
6. clear _____
7. gears _____
8. learn _____
9. bearer _____
10. smear _____
11. beard _____
12. earrings _____

Directions

Think of a word that fits each definition and has the sound of **ear** shown at the top of the column. Write the word in the boxes at the right. Some of the words may come from the list above, but others will not.

ear as in **ear**

1. a feeling of terror or fright
2. opposite of *far*
3. twelve months
4. to listen to sounds

f	e	a	r

ear as in **pear**

1. a large mammal with thick fur
2. to have on the body
3. to become torn
4. person or thing that carries

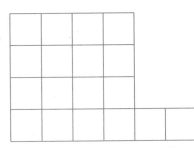

ear as in **pearl**

1. listened to
2. to look for
3. to gain knowledge
4. planet we live on

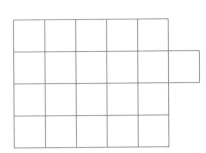

Write a word from the box that fits each definition.

rehearsal	bearded	earthenware
yearling	bearing	research
spearmint	forebears	rainwear

1. a plant used for flavoring _____

2. a one-year-old animal _____

3. practice for a play or speech _____

4. clothes for wet weather _____

5. people who lived before us; ancestors _____

6. dishes or jars made from baked clay _____

7. a careful investigation to find information _____

8. having hair growing on the lower part of the face _____

9. a part of a machine that helps another part to move _____

► **Directions**

Write the letter of the phrase that completes each sentence. Then circle each word that contains the letters **ear** and write the word in the correct column.

____ **10.** This year we will go   **a.** a bear.

____ **11.** We'll pack our gear and decide   **b.** what to wear.

____ **12.** In case of bad weather we should take   **c.** if we don't tear our clothes?

____ **13.** During our last trip we heard   **d.** our rainwear.

____ **14.** We learned to stay quiet,   **e.** to the Earth Trails Campground.

____ **15.** Will we earn any points   **f.** so we had no fear.

ear as in **appear**	**ear** as in **wear**	**ear** as in **search**
_____	_____	_____
_____	_____	_____
_____	_____	_____

Name  _____

> ▶ **Directions**
> Use the words from the box to complete the rhymes.

Rule The letters **air** and **are** can stand for the /air/ sound.
pair   dare

repair	Clare	fair	rare	declare	scare
Blair	flair	despair	mare	care	air

There once was a young boy named _____ ,

Who one day was heard to _____ ,

"I'll inflate a balloon,

While I'm singing a tune!"

Was young Blair just full of hot _____ ?

There was a sad girl in _____ ,

Who wanted to go to the _____ .

She got there by noon,

And then very soon,

She felt like she hadn't a _____ .

There once was a brave girl named _____ .

Who loved to ride her pet _____ .

The horse ran quite fast,

And as they flew past,

They gave everybody a _____ .

There once was a man with a _____ ,

Who could do any kind of _____ .

He fixed odds and ends,

For all of his friends.

They agreed that his talent was _____ .

Fill in the circle beside the word that completes each sentence.

1. The day dawned sunny and not very _____ on our farm.
   ○ cost   ○ cold   ○ mold

2. We planned to _____ a large birthday party that evening.
   ○ host   ○ ghost   ○ most

3. Grandma was seventy years _____.
   ○ told   ○ old   ○ kind

4. Then the _____ weather grew violent.
   ○ kind   ○ hold   ○ mild

5. A _____ blizzard sprang up and covered the land.
   ○ wind   ○ wild   ○ gold

6. "There will be no letters from the _____ office today," said Grandmother.
   ○ find   ○ fold   ○ post

7. "No, the carrier would get _____ in the snow and wind," replied Grandpa.
   ○ lost   ○ most   ○ mind

8. "How will people _____ us for the party?" asked Katya.
   ○ hind   ○ find   ○ grind

9. "I doubt anyone will get through," Grandpa _____ her.
   ○ told   ○ bold   ○ sold

10. "We will _____ another party in the spring," laughed Mother.
    ○ mold   ○ cold   ○ hold

11. Next morning, _____ of the high winds had stopped.
    ○ most   ○ ghost   ○ mild

12. Katya thought the bright sun might _____ her.
    ○ sold   ○ child   ○ blind

Lesson 11: Words with ILD, IND, OST, OLD

Name _____

▶ **Directions**

Read each word in the list. On the line in front of the word, write how many syllables it has. Then write the word in the correct column below.

Hint If you hear one vowel sound in a word, the word has one syllable. If you hear two vowel sounds, the word has two syllables, and so on.

1. ____ appear

2. ____ share

3. ____ repairing

4. ____ thunder

5. ____ calm

6. ____ binder

7. ____ flair

8. ____ sympathetic

9. ____ earring

10. ____ celebration

11. ____ youth

12. ____ astonishment

13. ____ accomplish

14. ____ poisonous

15. ____ mathematics

16. ____ carefully

One Syllable

_____

_____

_____

_____

Two Syllables

_____

_____

_____

_____

Three Syllables

_____

_____

_____

Four Syllables

_____

_____

_____

Study the rules. Then, divide the words into syllables using vertical lines.

Rule When two or more consonants come between two vowels in a word, the word is usually divided between the first two consonants.

bet/ter   wes/tern   per/mit   big/ger

Rule When a single consonant comes between two vowels in a word, the word is usually divided after the consonant if the first vowel is short.

nev/er   Phil/ip   shad/ow   rap/id

Rule When a single consonant comes between two vowels in a word, the word is usually divided before the consonant if the first vowel is long.

po/lar   na/tion   ra/zor   hu/mor

Rule When a consonant blend or consonant digraph comes between two vowels in a word, the word is usually divided after the blend or digraph if the first vowel is short, or before the blend or digraph if the first vowel is long.

moth/er   tick/et   di/graph   ze/bra

1. earnest _____   2. nectar _____

3. sentence _____   4. object _____

5. cartoon _____   6. shoulder _____

7. reward _____   8. photo _____

9. jacket _____   10. shiver _____

11. comic _____   12. either _____

13. rhubarb _____   14. cricket _____

15. quiver _____   16. brother _____

17. cabin _____   18. cheetah _____

Name _____

▶ **Directions**

Write the correct word from the box to complete each unfinished sentence.

their	year	physical	Greece
wreath	fair	written	race
Wrestling	fighting	eighty	earlier

The Olympics Then and Now

The first recorded Olympic Games were held in Greece in the _____
1

776 B.C. During that time, all the citizens of _____ would agree to a one-
2

month truce from _____ .
3

The Greeks held those _____ games to honor
4

_____ gods. The Greeks thought the _____ tests of
5   6

strength would please Zeus, the king of the gods.

The only event in the ancient Olympics was a _____ . Records show
7

that a man named Coroebus won the first race. He was crowned with an olive

_____ , which was a sign of peace. Poems and songs were
8

_____ to honor the winners of the Games.
9

In later years, other events were added to the competition. _____ and
10

track and field events were included. The judges that decided the winners of the events had to

be honest and _____ .
11

The modern Olympic Games are held every four years

in different places in the world. At that time, athletes from

more than _____ nations compete
12

against one another as the whole world watches.

Suppose you are a good enough athlete to train for the Olympic Games. Put a check by the event you would choose, or write your own idea.

_____ swimming   _____ marathon   _____ wrestling

_____ gymnastics   _____ hockey   _____ track and field

_____ bobsledding   _____ ice skating   _____ diving

_____ skiing   _____ basketball   _____
                                            (your idea)

▶ **Directions**

Use the words in the box to help answer the questions. Be sure to answer each question with a complete sentence.

dare	earnest	healthy	year	wear
careful	fair	youth	weary	athletic

1. Why did you choose this sport?

_____

_____

2. What qualities does a person need to succeed in this sport?

_____

_____

3. What types of clothing and equipment are needed?

_____

_____

4. How long and how often does a person need to practice the sport?

_____

_____

5. What advice would you give someone who wants to participate in this sport?

_____

_____

Name _____

▶ Directions

Write a word from the box to correctly complete each sentence. Use each word only once.

Rule A **vowel pair** follows the long vowel rule: When a syllable contains two vowels, the first vowel usually has the long sound of its name and the second vowel is silent.

The vowel pairs **ai** and **ay** follow the long vowel rule and can stand for the /ā/ sound.

p**ai**nt   **ay**

| gray | waited | stay | playful | acquaintances |
| delayed | mayor | Saturday | explain | rain |

1. More than two hundred citizens gathered at the park last _____.

2. The _____ was scheduled to make an important announcement.

3. She wanted to _____ the plans for building a new town library.

4. The crowd _____ patiently for the chief official to arrive.

5. Some people were feeling _____ and organized a ball game.

6. Others were content to chat with old

   _____.

7. Then the day turned cold and

   _____.

8. It began to _____ before the mayor arrived.

9. This _____ the mayor's speech.

10. Many people did not _____ to hear her talk.

▶ Directions

Underline each word in which **ai** stands for the /ā/ sound. Circle each word in which **ay** stands for the /ā/ sound.

waist	claim	may	painful	gnats	parcel
bay	bait	magnify	crayon	aid	paid
archway	daily	relay	Tuesday	taste	train
sailboat	scallops	faith	diagram	exclaim	dainty
playwright	braid	delay	gain	daisy	fake

Read each numbered word below. Write the word from the box that has the opposite meaning.

gain	display	fail	plain	playful	rainy
decay	daytime	stay	afraid	delay	daily

1. fancy _____

2. brave _____

3. conceal _____

4. leave _____

5. serious _____

6. nightly _____

7. nighttime _____

8. pass _____

9. sunny _____

10. flourish _____

11. begin _____

12. lose _____

▶ **Directions**

Each numbered word in the list below has something to do with transportation. Read each definition. Then write the letter of the correct definition by each word.

____ **13.** monorail

____ **14.** railway

____ **15.** driveway

____ **16.** sailboat

____ **17.** trail

____ **18.** alleyway

____ **19.** runway

____ **20.** subway

____ **21.** highway

____ **22.** trailer

a. a boat that is moved by one or more sails

b. a main road

c. an electric railroad running below the surface of city streets

d. a path hikers use

e. narrow back street in a city or town

f. a vehicle that is pulled behind a car

g. paved strip of land at an airport on which aircraft take off and land

h. path for cars that leads from a road to a garage or house

i. track made of rails

j. train that moves along on one rail

Name _____

Rule The vowel pairs **ee** and **ei** can stand for the /ē/ sound.
bee   ceiling

1. three   2. leisure   3. dungarees   4. proceed
5. seizure   6. weekly   7. pedigree   8. protein
9. wheels   10. ceiling   11. marquee   12. neither
13. steeple   14. breeze   15. agree

Directions

Use a word from the list above to answer each riddle.

16. Found in such foods
    As eggs, milk, and meat,
    It helps build strong bones,
    From our head to our feet.

    What is it? _____

17. If you want to know
    The name of the show,
    Look on the sign
    With its lights aglow.

    What is it? _____

18. Best of the breed and winner of fame,
    Sometimes a dog has papers that name
    The ancestry from which it came.

    What is it? _____

19. Cars and buses have them.
    Trucks and bikes do, too.
    Some have four, some have sixteen,
    and some have only two.

    What are they? _____

20. One plus two,
    Four minus one,
    Solve either problem.
    The riddle is done.

    What is the answer? _____

21. Time off from school,
    From work, from chores—
    It's time many people
    Spend outdoors.

    What is it? _____

22. Opposite the floor,
    High above your head,
    You may stare at this
    When you're in bed.
    What is it? _____

Find words in the puzzle that have the vowel pairs **ee** or **ei**. Some go across, and others go down. Circle each word you find. Then write the word in the correct column.

```
E  I  T  H  E  R  B  C  D  A  Z  L  M  N  G
B  O  E  B  F  E  E  T  L  L  F  G  D  B  C
D  R  I  F  G  C  P  N  M  L  F  G  D  B  C
T  H  T  G  R  E  E  D  N  H  A  F  R  E  E
L  C  H  G  L  I  Z  M  S  U  C  C  E  E  D
M  C  P  C  Z  P  H  X  E  Y  F  R  C  A  E
O  U  B  C  D  T  R  E  E  T  G  M  E  Z  X
A  B  Z  Y  X  W  Z  N  M  K  R  A  I  Y  E
D  E  C  E  I  V  E  L  S  T  Z  B  V  W  I
Z  T  G  M  C  V  O  E  R  N  W  M  E  E  T
```

ee words   **ei** words

_____   _____   _____

_____   _____   _____

_____   _____   _____

_____   _____   _____

▶ **Directions**

Write a word you found in the puzzle to complete each sentence.

1. I hope that I _____ a good grade on my paper.

2. I should get _____ an A or a B.

3. It _____ like I spent a month writing it!

4. I know it takes hard work to _____ .

5. This Saturday, however, I will enjoy some

_____ time.

Name _____

▶ **Directions**

Fill in the circle beside the word that best completes each sentence. Write it on the line.

Rule The vowel pairs **oa** and **oe** can stand for the /ō/ sound. The letters **ow** can also stand for the /ō/ sound.

loan   toe   flow

1. Jack is an athletic boy who is always _____ of his talents.
   ○ floating   ○ boasting   ○ outgrowing

2. He told everyone he got three strikes the last time he went _____ .
   ○ floating   ○ glowing   ○ bowling

3. He announced that he shot the _____ into the center of the target.
   ○ mistletoe   ○ minnow   ○ arrow

4. When he hit two home runs in a _____ , Jack made sure the whole school heard about it.
   ○ row   ○ hoe   ○ mow

5. He even notified the newspaper when he scored the most _____ on his soccer team.
   ○ goals   ○ toes   ○ glows

6. Most of Jack's classmates _____ when he begins talking.
   ○ grow   ○ toe   ○ groan

7. Some _____ away so they won't have to listen.
   ○ outgrow   ○ throat   ○ tiptoe

8. Others _____ up their hands in disgust.
   ○ tow   ○ toe   ○ throw

9. Even the _____ is getting tired of Jack's attitude.
   ○ loaves   ○ bowstring   ○ coach

10. He _____ shakes his head when he hears Jack start to brag.
   ○ slowly   ○ showed   ○ stowaway

Directions

Write the word from the box that names each picture. Then circle the letters that stand for the /ō/ sound.

boat	toaster	tiptoe	float
wheelbarrow	coach	arrow	bowling
doe	elbow	goal	snow
crowbar	loaves	soap	toad

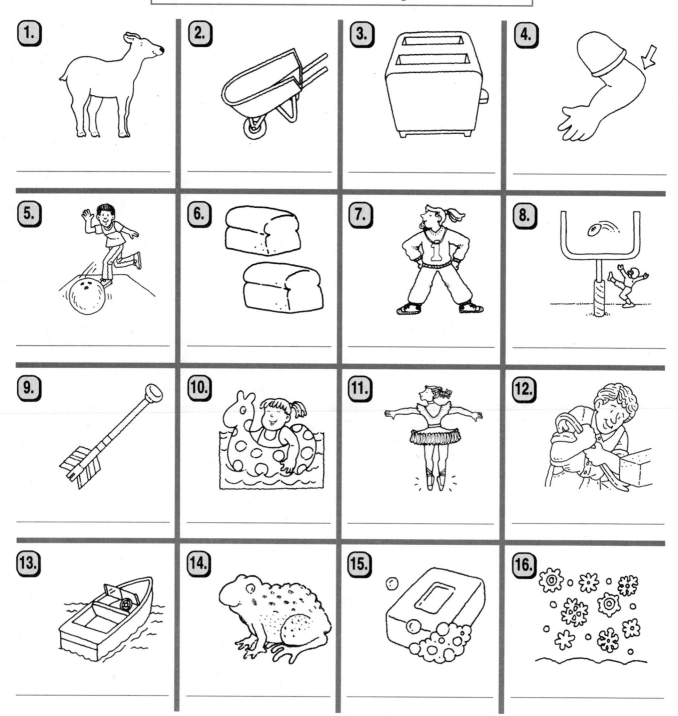

1.
2.
3.
4.
5.
6.
7.
8.
9.
10.
11.
12.
13.
14.
15.
16.

Name _____

away	Bay	boasting	ceilings	days
display	entertainment	fleeing	growing	narrow
rained	roads	succeeded	thrown	

The End of Pompeii

The Roman city of Pompeii was located

near the _____ 1 of Naples

in southern Italy, less than a mile

_____ 2 from the volcano,

Mount Vesuvius. In its early

_____ 3 , Pompeii was a

simple village with only a few inhabitants. In
time, Pompeii's pleasant scenery and good
climate attracted wealthy Romans to the city.
By the first century A.D., the city had

become a prosperous, _____ 4

community, _____ 5 large

homes, a busy marketplace, and several

theaters for _____ 6 .

Then, in A.D. 79, Vesuvius suddenly
erupted. Hot ashes, cinders, and stones

_____ 7 into the air by the

volcano _____ 8 down on

the city. Soon, _____ 9

were filled with people

_____ 10 for their lives.

Few were able to escape. Thousands of
people were killed by falling stones and
cinders or by poisonous fumes that came
from the volcano. Others were trapped in
their homes, crushed by falling

_____ 11 and walls. Even

those who _____ 12 in

getting outside were not saved. Debris was

falling into the _____ 13 streets.

The ashes and cinders that destroyed
Pompeii also preserved it. When they
cooled, these ashes and cinders formed a
layer that sealed up the city buried below.
The archaeologists who uncovered the ruins
much later found Pompeii just as it was on
the day Vesuvius erupted. Many items they

discovered are now on _____ 14
in a Naples museum.

Lesson 17: Review and write   **33**

This is your chance to practice good writing skills. Read the sentences and number them in the correct order. Then write each paragraph so the sentences tell the events that happened in the city of Pompeii in the correct sequence.

Hint Good writers revise their work by checking to see that what they wrote is well organized. They make sure that the items and events described are in the correct sequence, or order.

Paragraph 1

____ Hot ashes, cinders, and stones thrown into the air by the volcano rained down on the city.

____ Soon, roads were filled with people fleeing for their lives.

____ In A.D. 79, Vesuvius suddenly erupted.

Paragraph 2

____ Others were trapped in their homes, crushed by falling ceilings and walls.

____ Few, however, were able to escape.

____ Thousands of people were killed by falling ashes, stones, and cinders.

_____

_____

_____

_____

_____

_____

_____

_____

Name _____

 Directions

Write the word from the box that names each picture. Then circle the vowel sound you hear.

Rule In a **vowel digraph** two vowels together can make a long or short sound, or have a special sound all their own. Vowel digraphs don't always follow the long vowel rule. The vowel digraph **ea** can stand for the /ā/ sound, the /ē/ sound, or the /e/ sound.

st**ea**k m**ea**t br**ea**d

breakfast	peaches	steak	feather	sweater	wheat
seal	leash	eagle	pheasant	thread	break

1.
/ā/
/ē/
/e/

_____

2.
/ā/
/ē/
/e/

_____

3.
/ā/
/ē/
/e/

_____

4.
/ā/
/ē/
/e/

_____

5.
/ā/
/ē/
/e/

_____

6.
/ā/
/ē/
/e/

_____

7.
/ā/
/ē/
/e/

_____

8.
/ā/
/ē/
/e/

_____

9.
/ā/
/ē/
/e/

_____

10.
/ā/
/ē/
/e/

_____

11.
/ā/
/ē/
/e/

_____

12.
/ā/
/ē/
/e/

_____

▶ **Directions**

Use the words in the box to answer the questions. Use each word only once. Write /ā/, /ē/, or /e/ beside each word you write to show which sound the letters **ea** stand for.

steak	teacher	beagle	team
feathers	pleasant	wheat	breakfast
break	thread	beads	weather
leash	beaver		

1. What can you wear on a string around your neck?

_____

2. What are many kinds of bread made from?

_____

3. What might you use to walk your dog?

_____

4. What would you use to sew a rip in your shirt?

_____

5. Which word names a kind of meat?

_____

6. What is another name for a small dog with drooping ears?

_____

7. How could you describe a day that went well?

_____

8. Which word means the same as *smash*?

_____

9. What animal is known for building dams?

_____

10. What covers the body of birds?

_____

11. What do you call a group of people who play softball together?

_____

12. Which word refers to what is happening in the air outdoors?

_____

13. What meal do you eat in the morning?

_____

14. What do you call a person who helps students learn?

_____

Name _____

▶ Directions

Read the story. Circle each word in which the vowel digraph **ie** stands for the /ē/ sound. Draw a line under each word in which **ie** stands for the /ī/ sound.

Rule The vowel digraph **ie** can stand for the /ē/ sound or the /ī/ sound.
field   pie

Our Eventful Day

My brother and I wanted to drive the family car to the parade downtown, but Dad said, "No." We begged, but he would not yield, so we had to take the bus. We thought we would have a brief wait. Instead, we stood for an unbelievably long time at the bus stop. When the bus finally arrived, the driver apologized to the dissatisfied people. "I'm sorry this bus is late," he said. "Traffic was all tied up because of an accident."

As we got off the bus, two girls dashed past us shrieking and yelling, "Zeke! Stop! Someone grab our dog! His leash broke." We made a fierce effort to catch the little dog, but he soon disappeared, shielded by the crowd.

In spite of the confusion, we were on time for the parade. It was really exciting. The mayor led the parade. The fire chief drove a 1928 fire engine. Marching bands, led by girls wielding batons, tried for first place in the band competition. Clowns laughed and cried and performed tricks in the streets. We watched in disbelief as unicyclists applied their skill on the one-wheeled bikes. Some of the unicycles were so tall that their riders towered close to the tops of traffic lights and street lamps.

After the parade we stopped for sandwiches and French fries. As we paid the check, we spied the dog, Zeke, that had run away from the girls. He was sitting on the sidewalk looking at us through the window of the restaurant. We notified the police, who had the address of the owner.

Luckily for us, the owner of the dog was so relieved that she sent us a reward. If Dad had let us use the car, we would not have helped retrieve the dog. Then we would not be twenty-five dollars richer either. We really were more than satisfied.

Circle the vowel digraph **ie** in each word. Write /ī/ if **ie** stands for the long **i** sound. Write /ē/ if **ie** stands for the long **e** sound.

1. y i e l d _____

2. c r i e d _____

3. s a t i s f i e d _____

4. b r i e f _____

5. u n b e l i e v a b l e _____

6. f r i e d _____

7. s h r i e k i n g _____

8. d i s b e l i e f _____

9. c h i e f _____

10. f i e l d s _____

► Directions

Write a word from the list to complete each sentence.

11. Before the Pilgrims left their ship they signed a _____ agreement about the rules of the new settlement.

12. The eyes of the Pilgrims widened in _____ when they saw the deep forest and abundance of wild animals.

13. The Native American _____ promised that his tribe would help the settlers plant their crops.

14. The settlers of Plymouth worked hard to make sure the land would

_____ enough food.

15. When all the crops had been harvested, the Pilgrims were more than

_____ with their work.

16. _____ cornmeal mush was prepared over the campfires.

17. The little Pilgrim children began

_____ in excitement when they saw the dinner being prepared.

18. Although they were happy in their new home, it is hard for us to imagine the

_____ problems the Pilgrims lived with.

Name _____

Rule The vowel digraphs **ei** and **ey** can stand for the /ā/ sound.

rein   obey

rein	reign	they	disobey	prey	obey
skein	whey	vein	survey	convey	reindeer

Across

3. animal found in Greenland and some countries in northern Europe

4. to deliberately go against an order

7. a strap a horseback rider holds

10. thin, watery part of milk that appears when cheese is made

11. to take from one place to another

Down

1. a coil of yarn

2. to examine or inspect something

3. to rule over a country

5. to do what one is told

6. an animal that is hunted

8. a blood vessel that carries blood to the heart

9. a pronoun to describe persons, animals, or things

▶ **Directions**

Circle the correct word to complete each sentence. Then write the word on the line.

Rule The vowel digraphs **au** and **aw** both stand for the same sound of /aw/.

auto   cl**aw**s

1. The parade took place at the end of (autumn, author). _____

2. It was a blustery day and a (law, raw) wind was blowing. _____

3. Cars and floats (caught, crawled) along the parade route. _____

4. A celebrity waved from a shiny white (authority, automobile). _____

5. Her sequined (shawl, straw) sparkled in the sunlight. _____

6. Her fans (audience, applauded) wildly. _____

7. Then they pushed through the crowd to get her (autograph, automatic). _____

8. The star (cautioned, scrawled) her name for her admirers. _____

9. Later she had a conference with her (laundry, lawyer). _____

10. He (cautioned, haunted) her to review her contract carefully. _____

11. This rising young star often (fawns, flaunts) her success. _____

12. Her critics describe her as being (haughty, awning). _____

Name _____

► **Directions**

Read the article. Then write the correct word from the box to complete each unfinished sentence.

| laws | dried | libraries | authorities | Eastern | heavy |
| scrawling | great | breakable | chief | discoveries | read |

Early Writing

If you had been going to school in the seventh century B.C., in the Near

_____ land of
          1

Mesopotamia, you might have wanted to study in one of the

_____ . Instead of
          2

reading a book, you would have

_____ clay tablets
          3

containing wedge-shaped markings called *cuneiform* writing.

In Mesopotamia, people wrote with an instrument called a stylus, which was cut from a reed. They would press marks into damp clay. The rectangular clay tablets

were then _____ in the
                    4

sun or baked in an oven until they were hard.

How were the tablets used and what was written on them? The people of Mesopotamia used the tablets for recording

a _____ many different
          5

kinds of messages. For example,

government _____
                    6

used some tablets to record

_____ and rules.
          7

Using the tablets could be difficult. Because the tablets had to dry for several hours, writing was never simply a matter of

_____ down a
          8

message and sending it through the mail.

One of the _____
                          9

problems was the size and weight of the tablets. This made them too bulky and too

_____ to be easily
          10

carried from place to place. Storing the large tablets also was difficult, especially because the clay was brittle and quite

_____ . Because of
          11

these problems, the bulky tablets were stored in libraries.

One of the greatest

_____ of cuneiform
          12

inscriptions was the library of Nineveh, containing 25,000 tablets. This great library was established in the seventh century B.C., as a result of the endeavors of King Assurbanipal.

Hint Revising what you have written gives you a chance to make your writing more interesting and exciting to the reader.

When you read over what you have written, ask yourself:

Have I used some words too often?

Can I use different words to make my writing give the reader a better picture?

Can I think of other interesting details to help the reader better understand what I am trying to say?

▶ Directions

Read each pair of sentences. Circle the number of the sentence that gives a better picture.

1. People in ancient Mesopotamia pressed messages onto clay tablets.
2. In Mesopotamia people wrote messages on tablets.

3. The heavy clay tablets were too large to carry easily and a problem to store because they were breakable.
4. The tablets were heavy and not easy to store.

▶ Directions

Use details from the article on page 41 to revise the paragraph and make it more interesting.

In Mesopotamia, the difficulties of putting messages on tablets led to some of the earliest libraries. The clay had to have time to dry. Also, the tablets were heavy and hard to carry. Another problem was that the tablets were breakable. Storing the tablets in libraries helped solve these problems.

_____

_____

_____

_____

_____

_____

Name _____

 Directions

Show the sound that the vowel digraph **oo** stands for in each word. Write /o͞o/, /o͝o/, or /u/ on the line.

Rule   The vowel digraph **oo** can stand for the /o͞o/ sound as in **goose**, the /o͝o/ sound as in **look**, or the /u/ sound as in **blood**.

1. swoop _____   2. snoop _____   3. nook _____

4. brook _____   5. moody _____   6. swoon _____

7. tycoon _____   8. floodlight _____   9. neighborhood _____

10. moose _____   11. stood _____   12. loot _____

13. bassoon _____   14. bloodless _____   15. schooner _____

 Directions

Read the list of make-believe mystery cases. Circle each word that has the digraph **oo**. Then write each circled word in the correct column.

16. The Clue of the Snowy Footprints in the Woods

17. The Case of the Missing Driftwood in Gloomy Lagoon

18. The Mystery of the Crooked Footpath at Moonbeam Hill

19. The Missing Heirloom of Doom

20. The Bloodhound That Discovered the Pirates of Greenwood

21. The Case of the Gold Doubloons

22. The Mystery of the Flooded House

oo as in look

_____   _____   _____

_____   _____   _____

oo as in goose

_____   _____   _____

_____   _____   _____

oo as in flood

_____   _____   _____

Directions

Read each definition. Then write the word that matches the definition and contains the vowel sound shown by the symbol in front of the line.

1. a small furry animal with a long, bushy, ringed tail /o͞o/ _____

2. soft covering for the head /o͝o/ _____

3. small cage or pen for chickens /o͞o/ _____

4. a group of scouts /o͞o/ _____

5. male chicken /o͞o/ _____

6. a heavenly body that revolves around the earth /o͞o/ _____

7. a large dog with a keen sense of smell /u/ _____

8. mark made by a foot /o͝o/ _____

9. a swimming bird similar to a duck /o͞o/ _____

10. covering for foot and lower leg /o͞o/ _____

11. a tool to sweep with /o͞o/ _____

12. the opposite of *bad* /o͝o/ _____

13. you throw a basketball into it /o͞o/ _____

14. a small stream /o͝o/ _____

15. not tight /o͞o/ _____

Name _____

▶ **Directions**

Read each sentence. Underline the words in which **ui** sounds like the **ui** in br**ui**se and circle the words in which **ui** sounds like the **ui** in g**ui**lty. Then write each word in the correct column.

Rule The vowel digraph **ui** can stand for the /i/ sound or the /o͞o/ sound.

build   juice

1. My father just built a new restaurant.
2. The unusual building attracts many customers.
3. It was designed to look like a cruise ship.
4. In bad weather, however, it doesn't shake or quiver.
5. Customers must wear suitable clothing.
6. Bathing suits are not allowed.
7. The specialty is thick, juicy steaks.
8. The crisp, light biscuits are in demand.
9. The fresh fruit salad is also very popular.
10. The food is always served very quickly.
11. Customers enjoy listening to the guitar music.
12. No one ever causes a nuisance.

bruise   **guilty**

_____   _____

_____   _____

_____   _____

_____   _____

_____   _____

| bruise | quilt | nuisance | suits | cruising |
| suitably | building | guilty | pursuit | build |

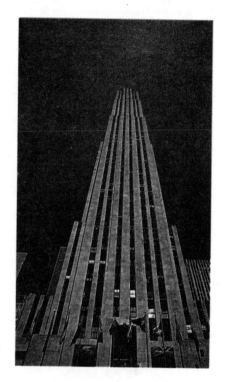

Across
3. something or someone that causes bother
6. an activity to which someone gives time and energy
7. construct something
8. sets of clothes to be worn together
9. having done something wrong

Down
1. a covering for a bed
2. a structure
4. properly
5. sailing around
7. an injury that discolors the skin

Directions

Underline the words in which **ui** sounds like the **ui** in b**ui**ld and circle the words in which **ui** sounds like the **ui** in j**ui**ce.

fruit   mannequins   biscuits   exquisite
circuit   cruise   suitable   quilt
built   guitar   guilty   bruise
pursuit   recruit   cruiser   building

Name _____

| wool | roof | harpoons | juices | fruits | blood |
| suited | built | livelihood | footbridges | food | good |

The Great Inca Empire

Several thousand years ago, a group of primitive people living in what is now South

America earned their _____ 1 by hunting and fishing. Their weapons

were bows and arrows, sticks, and _____ 2 . Little by little, those

people—called the Incas—developed a great empire. By the time the Spaniards came to the

"New World," the Incas ruled one of the largest and richest empires in the Americas.

Their capital city of Cuzco, in what is now Peru, was so high up in the mountains that the

Incas were said to be living on the "_____ 3 of the world." Because of

the high altitude, the weather was extremely cold. Clothing _____ 4 to

the climate was made from the _____ 5 of the alpaca or the llama.

However, the Inca ruler and those of noble _____ 6 wore clothes made

from the fleece of the vicuña.

The Incas who lived along the coast, though, did not need heavy, warm clothes. They made

clothing from cotton that they wove and then dyed with the _____ 7 of

berries and certain _____ 8 and vegetables.

The Incas were skillful farmers. Potatoes were a main _____ 9 .

Other crops raised by the Incas included corn, beans, and tomatoes. The Incas not only

farmed the mountain valleys, but they also planted crops on the terraces which they had

_____ 10 on the steep mountainsides.

There were many talented engineers among the Incas. Due to their skills, a

_____ 11 road system connected all parts of the empire with the capital.

_____ 12 , built by the engineers, still look the same as they did

centuries ago.

Pretend you are a newspaper reporter living thousands of years ago in South America. You have traveled to the Inca empire and want to write an article about it. Use the main ideas listed in the box below to write a three-paragraph article about the Incas. Be sure the sentences in each paragraph support the main idea. If they do not, rewrite the sentences or leave them out.

The Incas have an advanced civilization. The Incas are skillful farmers. The Incas are also good engineers.

Name _____

▶ **Directions**

Read each word. Circle the diphthong **oi** or **oy**.
Then write the word from the box that matches
the definition.

Definition A **diphthong**
consists of two vowels blended
together as one vowel sound. The
diphthongs **oi** and **oy** stand for the
same vowel sound.

coin   boy

corduroy	turquoise	royalty	poison	spoil	embroidery
moisten	asteroids	annoy	sequoia	voyage	enjoyable

1. small planets that revolve around the sun

   between Mars and Jupiter _____

2. greenish-blue stone used for jewelry _____

3. a thick cotton cloth with velvet-like ridges _____

4. to bother, or to make a bit angry

   _____

5. to damage or to ruin

   _____

6. that which provides pleasure

   _____

7. an evergreen tree that
   can grow very tall _____

8. those who have the powers of a king or queen

   _____

9. a journey or trip

   _____

10. designs sewn into cloth with a needle and thread

    _____

11. something that can cause illness or death

    _____

12. to make something damp or a bit wet

    _____

▶ Directions

Circle the correct ending for each
analogy and write it on the line.

Definition An **analogy** compares
different things. Analogies show how
pairs of things are alike.
Puppy is to **dog** as **kitten** is to **cat**.

1. **Strawberry** is to **fruit** as **redwood** is to —————————.
   foil   spoil   sequoia

2. **Asteroid** is to **sun** as **moon** is to —————————.
   loyal   earth   enjoy

3. **Corduroy** is to **pants** as **turquoise** is to —————————.
   annoy   toil   ring

4. **Brush** is to **painting** as **needle** is to —————————.
   embroidery   ointment   moist

5. **Happy** is to **sad** as **satisfy** is to —————————.
   appoint   disappoint   disappointment

6. **Queen** is to **royalty** as **dime** is to —————————.
   coin   join   noisemaker

7. **Oyster** is to **ocean** as **earthworm** is to —————————.
   spoil   broil   soil

▶ Directions

Complete this analogy.

8. **Boat** is to **water** as **car** is to —————————.

Name _____

 Directions

Read each word in the box. Circle the diphthong **ou**
or **ow.** Then write the word from the box that names
each picture.

Rule The diphthongs **ou** and
ow often stand for the vowel
sound you hear in **ou**t and sc**ow**l.

sunflower	trout	owl	mountain
clouds	vowels	fountain	plow

1.

_____

2.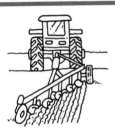

_____

3.

_____

4.

_____

5.

_____

6.

_____

7.

_____

8.

_____

Read the words in each row. Draw a line under the two words that have the same vowel sound. Then circle the letters that stand for the sound.

1. cowl   foul   glamour
2. devout   four   grouch
3. pout   growl   dough
4. tower   sew   renown
5. owe   out   powder
6. chowder   soup   mountain
7. touch   prowl   towel
8. cowboy   bounty   dozen
9. scowl   enormous   fowl
10. journey   frown   profound
11. eyebrow   crouch   coupon
12. soupy   snout   allowance
13. recount   how   flown
14. endow   tough   shout
15. doubt   cougar   coward

▶ **Directions**

Write a phrase from the box to answer each question.

loud crowd	hound sound
cow chow	shower flower

16. What would you call the howl from a hunting dog? _____

17. What would you call a very noisy group of people? _____

18. What would you call feed for a herd of cattle? _____

19. What would you call a plant that blooms only when it rains? _____

Name _____

▶ Directions

Complete the crossword puzzle by finding the **ew** word in the box that fits each description. You will not need to use every word.

Rule The diphthong **ew** stands for the vowel sound you hear in **few**. It is nearly the same vowel sound you hear in **moon**.

renewal	newspaper	few	shrewd	steward	mildew
flew	pewter	dew	drew	nephew	chew
jeweler	crew	yew	blew	views	new

Across

4. what you do to food before swallowing it

5. person who makes, sells, or repairs necklaces and watches

8. making something new or fresh again

9. clever or wise

11. kind of furry, white fungus that appears during damp weather

12. type of evergreen tree or shrub

Down

1. the news of the day is printed in this

2. a grayish metal made by mixing tin with lead, brass, or copper

3. opposite of *many*

4. group of sailors working on a ship

6. the son of a person's sister or brother

7. past tense of *fly*

10. past tense of *draw*

Write the number of syllables you hear in each word. Then write the vowel pair, vowel digraph, or diphthong that each word contains.

	Syllables Heard	Vowel Pair or Digraph, or Diphthong		Syllables Heard	Vowel Pair or Digraph, or Diphthong
1. juice	_____	_____	2. woodpecker	_____	_____
3. fellows	_____	_____	4. account	_____	_____
5. counter	_____	_____	6. treason	_____	_____
7. reign	_____	_____	8. pheasant	_____	_____
9. down	_____	_____	10. retrieve	_____	_____
11. portray	_____	_____	12. survey	_____	_____
13. treat	_____	_____	14. dauntless	_____	_____
15. waterproof	_____	_____	16. withdrew	_____	_____
17. disobey	_____	_____	18. seamstress	_____	_____
19. treachery	_____	_____	20. reasonable	_____	_____
21. sluice	_____	_____	22. occupied	_____	_____
23. essay	_____	_____	24. board	_____	_____
25. thesaurus	_____	_____	26. gingerbread	_____	_____
27. breaker	_____	_____	28. mayhem	_____	_____
29. withdraw	_____	_____	30. thundercloud	_____	_____
31. refugee	_____	_____	32. greedy	_____	_____
33. schoolmaster	_____	_____	34. growth	_____	_____
35. author	_____	_____	36. however	_____	_____
37. soapy	_____	_____	38. tomorrow	_____	_____
39. oboe	_____	_____	40. upheaval	_____	_____
41. shower	_____	_____	42. feast	_____	_____
43. applause	_____	_____	44. appoint	_____	_____
45. shook	_____	_____	46. hawthorn	_____	_____
47. renew	_____	_____	48. authentic	_____	_____

Name _____

Directions

Read the article. Write the correct word from the box to complete each unfinished sentence. Then write each word in the correct column to show which diphthong it contains.

| loyal | throughout | powerful | shrewd | overpowered |
| count | appointed | views | new | |

Alexander the Great

By the time he was 30, Alexander the Great ruled a huge empire. In a very few years, he and his troops had

_____ the armies of
        1

the greatest kingdoms in Europe and the Middle East. He had conquered most of the lands from Greece to India. When he died at 32, his accomplishments were known

_____ the world.
        2

Alexander had great strength, intelligence, and pride. He was determined, even as a boy, to outdo the accomplishments of his father, Philip, the

_____ and
        3

_____ king of
        4

Macedonia. Alexander became king when he was only 20. At the time, Greece was divided into small city-states. Alexander acted swiftly and firmly to unite the Greek

cities and to make sure they would be

_____ to him.
        5

Next, he moved east to conquer Persia, and then to Egypt. The Egyptians welcomed

him and he could _____
                          6

on their support. Finally he led his troops into India.

Alexander had grand plans for his empire. He encouraged the spread of Greek

_____, customs,
        7

and laws into Asia. He also brought

_____ ideas from
        8

Asia back to Europe. He tried to be a just

king; he _____ officials
                   9

he felt would be honest and fair.

Alexander died of malaria when he was only 32. He will always be remembered as an outstanding general and a great king.

ou as in **ground**   **ew** as in **grew**   **oy** as in **royal**   **ow** as in **brown**   **oi** as in **oil**

_____   _____   _____   _____   _____

_____   _____   _____   _____

_____

The following sentences tell about Alexander the Great. They are not written in the order in which the events happened. Number the sentences in the correct sequence, and write them as a paragraph on the lines below.

Definition Sequence is the order in which things happen. When you write, it is important to put facts and details in the correct sequence.

_____ Four years later, at the age of 18, Alexander led troops into battle and then became ambassador to Athens, Greece.

_____ When he was 14, he began studying under Aristotle, a great teacher and important philosopher.

_____ Alexander was born in 356 B.C. in Macedonia.

_____ After creating a vast empire stretching from Greece to India, Alexander died of malaria in 323 B.C., at 32 years of age.

_____ At the age of 20, Alexander became the king of Macedonia.

_____ He was the son of Philip of Macedon, a fearless general, and Olympias, a princess.

Name _____

▶ Directions

Study the outline. Then read each sentence and circle the answer that best completes it.
Write the answer on the line.

Units of Meaning in Words

I. Basic parts of words

    A. A **base word** is a *word* to which word parts may be added.

        1. The base word of **uncover** is **cover.**

        2. The base word of **unlawful** is **law.**

    B. A **root** is a *word part* to which other word parts may be added.

        1. The root of **induction** is **duct.**

        2. The root of **important** is **port.**

II. Prefixes

    A. A **prefix** is a word part added to the *beginning* of a base word or root.

    B. A prefix may have one or more letters.

    C. A prefix changes the meaning of a base word or root.

        1. The prefix in **unwrap** is **un.**

        2. The prefix in **ablaze** is **a.**

III. Suffixes

    A. A **suffix** is a word part added to the *end* of a base word or root.

    B. A suffix may have one or more letters.

    C. A suffix changes the meaning of a base word or root.

        1. The suffix in **joyful** is **ful.**

        2. The suffix in **exports** is **s.**

---

1. The base word of **unspeakable** is _____.

        un   speak   able

---

2. The root of **dictator** is _____.

        dict   ator   or

---

3. The prefix in **foresee** is _____.

        fore   see   foresee

---

4. The suffix in **unreadable** is _____.

        un   read   able

---

5. The root of **transportation** is _____.

        trans   port   ation

Circle the answer that best completes each sentence. Then write it on the line.

1. **Pre** is the prefix in **precooks** and **predicted.** The base word of

   precooks is _____ .

           pre   cook   s

2. The root of **predicted** is _____ .

           pre   dict   ed

3. **Mis** is the prefix in **mistake.** The word **mistaken**

   has _____ word part(s).

   one   two   three

4. A base word _____ a word itself.

           is   is not

5. A root _____ *always* a word itself.

       is   is not

6. The word **prepackaged** has _____ word parts.

         two   three   four

7. The word **unmistakable** has four word parts including _____ prefixes.

         two   three   four

8. **En** is the prefix of **enlarge.** The word **enlargement** has _____ word parts.

         two   three   four

Directions

Rewrite each word putting vertical lines between the word parts.

9. enforce _____

10. untrue _____

11. forceful _____

12. misplace _____

13. forcefully _____

14. renewable _____

15. reinforcing _____

16. entrust _____

17. reinforcement _____

18. singing _____

19. unbeatable _____

20. rightful _____

21. inscribe _____

22. player _____

Name _____

▶ **Directions**

Complete each sentence by choosing a prefix from the box to add to the word below the line. Then write the word on the line.

Rule Ir, im, il, and in are prefixes that usually mean *not*.

irregular = not regular
imperfect = not perfect
illegal = not legal
inexpensive = not expensive

ir	im	il	in

1. Phil thought that Saturday's airplane flight would be an _____

significant
   event.

2. Friday night, however, Phil found it _____ to avoid dreaming

possible
   about airplanes.

3. Phil's dream may have been _____, but it was exciting.

rational

4. Although Phil is an _____ pilot, he was flying a jet in his

experienced
   dream.

5. It is highly _____ for a young boy to be the pilot of a jet.

regular

6. Since Phil didn't have a license, it was _____ for him to fly

legal
   the plane.

7. All of a sudden, Phil was _____ of controlling the plane.

capable

8. Heavy fog had made the airport _____.

visible

9. Phil felt _____ because he couldn't read the instruments

effective
   very well.

10. It was an _____ landing, but the plane and passengers were

perfect
    safe.

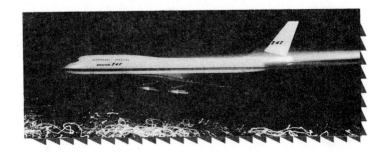

Read the story. Circle each word with a prefix that means *not*.

Michael Faraday

Michael Faraday is known as a great scientist, but the first job he held may have been the same as your first job. He was a news carrier. He worked irregular hours for low pay. In the early 1800s, news carriers took their papers from door to door and waited while each client read the newspaper before taking it to the next customer. This was an inexpensive way for people to read the news, but it was inconvenient for news carriers like Michael.

Later, Faraday became a bookbinder. Bookbinding taught him to work slowly and carefully. He could not be impatient or inexact. As he worked, he became curious about the contents of the books. Faraday had no schooling, so he was nearly illiterate. Although his reading skills were imperfect, he kept practicing. He finally taught himself to read. He read every book that came to the bindery. His favorite topic was science. Faraday yearned to be a scientist, but that seemed impossible.

One day Faraday met Sir Humphry Davy, a famous scientist. Davy was astonished at what Faraday knew about science. He let Faraday be his assistant.

Soon Faraday became a full-fledged scientist. He worked to find a way to use electricity as a source of energy. He was a brilliant experimenter, but his work was incomplete because he did not know enough mathematics. Many other scientists of his time thought his experiments were interesting, but inapplicable to daily life. His experiments proved to be of inestimable value, however. They eventually led to inventions such as the telephone, electric light, TV, and the computer.

Directions

Find a word you circled that fits each definition.

1. _____ not perfect

2. _____ not the usual

3. _____ not suitable to everyday things

4. _____ not costing a lot of money

5. _____ not patient

6. _____ not able to be estimated

7. _____ not able to read

8. _____ not handy or easy to do

Name _____

▶ Directions

Ten words with the prefix **im** or **em** are hidden in the puzzle. Some of the words go across and some go down. Circle each word as you find it in the puzzle. Then write the word beside its meaning.

Rule
The prefixes **im** and **em** usually mean *in, into,* or *on.* Remember, **im** can also mean *not.*

immigration   = people coming into a country
immeasurable = not measurable
embed   = set something firmly into

```
E R V B S L O T U N I N L
M L X Z B T C I C D M N T
L E B I M M E R S E P O R
I K E M B R O I D E R Y C
M S R P A R B E M B O S S
I M P R O V I S E I P X A
A I M O M I M P U R E E R
J E I B E V I M P O R T B
T A N A N S F G H U Y I Z
L E M B R A C E M I S R W
H E W L I M P E R I L R T
T G X E C Z L N S B C Y G
```

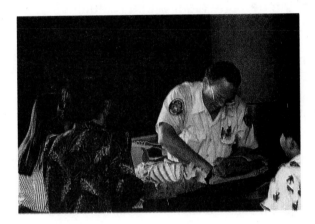

1. _____ to put a decoration or raised design on an article

2. _____ to sink into water

3. _____ not pure

4. _____ to bring in something from another country

5. _____ to put in danger

6. _____ to hug

7. _____ needlework

8. _____ not correct or right

9. _____ not likely to happen

10. _____ to perform something with no preparation

Directions

Write a word from the box to complete each sentence.

immaturely	immigrated	emerged	embark	imagined
employing	improbable	empowered	important	immerse
immediately	impatience	improved	embedded	embraced

1. Miguel often ______________________ taking a great vacation with his family.
2. It was ______________________ to Miguel to spend time with his family.
3. Miguel thought the chances of a vacation this year were ______________________ .
4. Miguel's father ______________________ from the den one night with a handful of maps.
5. "We are going to ______________________ on a fantastic vacation," Miguel's father said.
6. "______________________ after work tomorrow, we will leave."
7. Miguel was so happy he ______________________ his father.
8. Miguel waited for the next day with great ______________________ .
9. He didn't want to act ______________________ , however, so he kept his thoughts to himself.
10. ______________________ in Miguel's mind were his father's words "fantastic vacation."

Directions

Now write three sentences of your own. In each sentence, include at least one of the **em** or **im** words from the sentences above.

11. ____

____

12. ____

____

13. ____

____

Name _____

Directions

Circle each word in which **mis** or **mal** is used as a prefix.

Rule The prefixes **mis** and **mal** usually mean *bad* or *badly*, or *wrong* or *wrongly*.
mispronounce = pronounce wrongly
maladjustment = bad adjustment

1. mispronounce	2. male	3. misunderstand	4. Maltese
5. malodorous	6. mislabel	7. malformation	8. misbehave
9. malnourished	10. misread	11. malpractice	12. maltreat
13. missile	14. mallet	15. maladjusted	16. misery
17. malnutrition	18. misspelling	19. malfunction	20. misquote

Directions

Write the word from the above list that best completes each sentence.

21. People often ignore or _____ the right methods for caring for dogs.

22. Moving to a new home can cause a dog to become _____.

23. If you _____ your dog, it might become aggressive.

24. A _____ puppy is in danger of sickness and abnormal development.

25. Proper grooming and hygiene should correct any _____ smells.

26. If your dog needs medicine, be careful not to _____ the directions.

27. _____ is often the cause of poor bone development.

28. Your dog will not _____ if it has been properly trained.

Use the words in the box to work the crossword puzzle.

misinform	misdeed	malformation	malnutrition
misjoin	misdo	malodorous	misdiagnose
maltreats	mislaid	mistrial	misname

Across

2. to call by a wrong name
5. bad-smelling
6. to decide incorrectly after an examination
7. to give out the wrong information
8. poor nourishment; not enough good food

Down

1. treats badly
3. lost; out of place
4. wrong or unusual formation
5. a trial having no effect in law because some part of it was conducted incorrectly

Name _____

▶ **Directions**

Read the story. Circle each word that begins with the prefix **ir, im, il, in, em, mis,** or **mal.**
You will circle fifteen words.

The European Adventurers

In the early 1500's, many adventure-seeking people embarked for the New World from Europe. They faced many troubles at sea. Inaccurate instruments often caused them to misjudge directions. Sometimes, lost at sea for weeks, they were forced to eat things we would consider inedible, such as dry or moldy biscuits. Fierce storms sometimes imperiled their ships. The explorers often faced misfortune with immeasurable courage. Unfortunately, these courageous sailors did a poor job of understanding and preserving the new cultures they discovered.

Sometimes the sailors caused irreparable damage to the way of life of the native people in Central and South America. For example, the natives were exposed to smallpox, a disease against which they had no immunity. Also, to the great misfortune of the natives, the sailors destroyed magnificent temples and melted down statues made of gold. They burned books which embodied the history and beliefs of the Mayans. Because of the insensitivity and indifference of the European sailors, these irrecoverable artifacts were destroyed forever. Today it is impossible to regain the rich store of knowledge and art that formed the remarkable Mayan culture.

▶ **Directions**

Read each sentence about the story. If it is correct, write **true.** If it is incorrect, write **false.**

1. Many European adventurers were brave._____

2. Life at sea was difficult in the early 1500's._____

3. Precise instruments were needed to make navigation easier. _____

4. All sailors treated the natives of Central and

   South America very kindly. _____

5. We have gained vast knowledge about the Maya from the careful records the exploring

   sailors kept. _____

Combine a sentence on the left with one on the right by using one of the connecting words from the box. Write your sentence on the lines below. Remember to use a comma before the connecting word in your new sentence.

Hint Two sentences can often be combined into one sentence for smoother reading by using a connecting word such as **and** or **but**.

and = also, in addition to, plus	**so** = as a result
yet = still, but	**but** = yet, however

1. Almost all the Maya farmed.
2. The Maya did not have wheeled vehicles.
3. The Maya believed that astronomy was important.
4. The houses the Maya built were really square or oval huts.
5. Long ago, Mayan cities teemed with life.

a. They compiled accurate tables of dates on which to expect eclipses of the sun.
b. Many of them also kept hives of stingless bees for honey.
c. Today all that remain are ruins deep in the jungle.
d. They built wide, stone-surfaced roads.
e. The walls were made of poles that were sometimes coated with mud.

Name _____

Directions

Write a word from the box to complete each sentence.

Rule The prefixes **anti** and **counter** mean *against* or *opposite*.

antipollution = against pollution
counterclockwise = in the opposite direction that the clock runs

---

counterbalance	antipollution	counteroffers	antiknock	countermeasure
counterpart	counterclockwise	antilock	antifreeze	antiseptic

1. My brother found a used car with _____ brakes to keep the wheels from locking.

2. Its _____ devices limit dangerous exhaust fumes.

3. During the test drive, he turned the wheel clockwise and _____ to check the steering.

4. He checked the weights on the tire rims that _____ the wheels to keep them from wobbling.

5. After several offers and _____, my brother bought the car.

6. As a _____ against tire problems, my brother bought a spare.

7. On the way home, he bought gas with _____ ingredients to keep the engine from knocking.

8. At home, I helped my brother put _____ in the car to protect the engine in cold weather.

9. We installed one headlight, but we broke its _____.

10. My brother cut his hand on the glass and had to put an _____ on it.

1. The car engine is cold from the wintery breeze.

   What that engine needs quick is some _____.

2. Poor Sue is sick. What can she do?

   The doctor may prescribe an _____ or two.

3. John thought his chess playing did really improve

   Till Jill captured his king in a _____.

countermove
antifreeze
antibiotic

_____ 4. Which sentence gives a **counterproposal?**
   a. I think our kitchen cabinets need to be replaced.
   b. I disagree that we should buy a new car, but perhaps we might buy a used car.
   c. I think we should buy a new radio.

_____ 5. Which sentence expresses **antipathy?**
   a. I hate spiders!
   b. My new roller skates are gone.
   c. Greg prefers hiking off the trails.

_____ 6. Which sentence expresses **antisocial** feelings?
   a. Come to my party.
   b. Leave me alone.
   c. Do your homework.

_____ 7. Which sentence contains a **countersign?**
   a. Saturday will be sunny and warm.
   b. We have five more months of school.
   c. The password is "cheeseburger."

_____ 8. Which sentence supports **antilittering** laws?
   a. Litter is a part of life.
   b. Our city fines people who throw trash into the streets.
   c. Empty soda cans and newspapers are scattered all over the park.

Name _____

 **Directions**

Write the correct word from the box on the line beside its definition.

Rule The prefix **de** can mean *down* or *away*.
descend = go down
depart = go away

defroster	dejected	delay	detour	departed	descending

1. _____ a substitute route

2. _____ to put off or postpone

3. _____ depressed

4. _____ the act of moving down

5. _____ to have gone away or left

6. _____ a device to remove ice or frost

Directions

Write a word from the box to complete each sentence.

7. Our bus _____ for the football game at 6:00 a.m.

8. The windows were covered with ice because the _____ was broken.

9. Because of road construction, we were forced to take a _____ .

10. _____ the steep hill, we hoped the brakes would work.

11. A flat tire caused a two-hour _____ .

12. Even though we missed the game, we were cheerful and not _____ .

Directions

Circle each word that contains the prefix **de**.

dean	deodorize	dealt	decimal	deflate	dear
decamp	denounce	dentist	debrief	derailed	decrease
decade	decry	defrost	decode	depth	dehumidifier
departure	denim	deplane	detach	dethrone	detract

Directions

Use the words in the box to complete the crossword puzzle.

Across

2. to figure out the meaning of something that is written in secret writing
5. a machine that takes moisture out of the air
6. to get off an airplane
7. to unfasten or disconnect
8. to let air out

Down

1. to take away or cover up the smell of something
3. to take away or make less
4. to remove frost or ice
5. a going away or leaving

Name _____

 Directions

Circle the word that fits the definition.
Then write the word on the line.

Rule The prefix **fore** means *front* or *before*.
Post means *after*.

   forenoon = before noon

   postwar = after a war

               postpone

1. _____ to put off until later   forecast

               posterity

               foreword

2. _____ to alert to danger beforehand   forecast

               forewarn

               foremost

3. _____ first; chief; leading   postpone

               forecast

               posterity

4. _____ a thought added after a letter is written   postpone

               postscript

 Directions

Circle the correct ending for each analogy.
Then write the answer on the line.

Definition An **analogy** compares different things. Analogies show how pairs of things are alike. For example:
True is to **false** as **top** is to **bottom**.

5. **Postpone** is to **delay** as **deliver** is to _____.

               bring   stop   cancel

6. **Best** is to **worst** as **foremost** is to _____.

               first   last   next

7. **Predawn** is to **dawn** as **forenoon** is to _____.

               right   noon   lunch

8. **Forecast** is to **predict** as **shout** is to _____.

               remember   whisper   yell

9. **Foreground** is to **near** as **background** is to _____.

               painting   distant   backyard

Choose the word from the box that completes each sentence. Write the letters of the words on the lines.

foremost	posterity	forefinger	foreshadow	forewarned
postgraduate	foretell	forehead	postpone	foresight

1. We hoped the rain on Friday did not ___ ___ ___ ___ ___ ◯ ___ ___ ___ ___ a terrible weekend.

2. Not even the meteorologist could ___ ___ ___ ___ ___ ___ ◯ ___ the weekend weather.

3. We made a group decision not to ___ ___ ___ ◯ ___ ___ ___ ___ our camping trip.

4. Frank had the ___ ___ ___ ___ ___ ___ ◯ ___ ___ to suggest that we pack our rain gear.

5. Lucas wanted to film our trip for ___ ___ ___ ___ ◯ ___ ___ ___ ___ .

6. He filmed a ranger with a bandanna across her ___ ___ ___ ___ ◯ ___ ___ ___ .

7. The ranger ___ ◯ ___ ___ ___ ___ ___ ___ ___ us that swimming in the river was dangerous.

8. She told us about the park's ___ ___ ___ ___ ___ ___ ◯ ___ hiking trails.

9. She pointed to the best trail with her ___ ___ ___ ___ ___ ◯ ___ ___ ___ .

10. She explained that she had learned about becoming a ranger when she was a ___ ___ ___ ___ ___ ___ ___ ___ ◯ ___ ___ ___ student.

▶ **Directions**

Answer the riddle by writing each circled letter above the number of its sentence.

Riddle

What house weighs the least?

Answer

The ___ ___ ___ ___ ___ ___ ___ ___ ___ ._ ___
   2 9 4 6 3 1 7 10 8 5

Name _____

▶ **Directions**

Read the story. Circle each word that begins with one of the following prefixes: **fore, post, de, counter, anti.**

Antibiotics

An antibiotic is a drug produced by or made from tiny living things, especially from molds. An antibiotic helps the body defend itself against dangerous germs. There are many different antibiotics, but penicillin is the foremost one. Antibiotics are called "wonder drugs" because they have caused a decline in so many diseases. For example, bacterial pneumonia and scarlet fever once deprived thousands of people of healthy lives each year. Now these diseases can be treated and cured almost as soon as they are detected. Postoperative infections were once as dangerous as surgery itself. Now these, too, can be cured.

Taking too much or too little of an antibiotic does not help the body. In fact, it is counterproductive. If germs have a chance to build up a resistance to the antibiotic, it becomes useless so it's important to take the exact amount prescribed by your doctor.

Many doctors forewarn against antibiotics being used too freely—especially in many countries where they can be bought without a prescription from a doctor. The power of antibiotics in these countries has greatly decreased. Scientists must devote more research to finding new and more effective antibiotics to counteract germs.

▶ **Directions**

Write a word that you circled that matches each definition.

1. _____ a drug that fights germs

2. _____ took away

3. _____ became less

4. _____ guard from harm; keep safe

5. _____ to act against or opposite

6. _____ first; leading

7. _____ warn beforehand

8. _____ occurring after a surgical operation

9. _____ discovered

10. _____ interfering with reaching a goal

Directions

Combine each pair of sentences. Use the word in boldface print as your connecting word. Usually a comma is used before the connecting words **and** and **but,** but not before the word **because.**

Hint Two sentences can often be combined into one sentence for smoother reading.

1. Antibiotics are called "wonder drugs." They have a wonderful ability to destroy disease germs quickly.   **because**

_____

_____

2. At first, only small amounts of antibiotics could be made. Drug manufacturers now produce them in huge quantities.   **but**

_____

_____

3. Penicillin is the antibiotic that is the least poisonous to people. It is probably the most widely used.   **and**

_____

_____

Directions

Combine each sentence pair below using your own connecting word.

4. Alexander Fleming discovered penicillin in 1928. He shared the 1945 Nobel Prize in medicine for the development of this antibiotic.

_____

_____

_____

5. The price of 100,000 units of penicillin was once twenty dollars. Today that amount costs much less.

_____

_____

_____

Name _____

▶ Directions

Add the prefix at the top of the column to each word in the column. Write the new word on the line.

Rule The prefix **over** means *too* or *too much*. The prefix **ultra** means *beyond* or *very*. The prefix **super** can mean *very, over, or greater than others.*

overcrowded = too crowded
ultrafine = very fine
supercold = very cold
supersonic = traveling more than the speed of sound

1. over

time _____
cautious _____
confident _____
load _____

2. ultra

modern _____
light _____
violet _____
critical _____

3. super

market _____
star _____
sonic _____
highway _____

▶ Directions

Use one of the words you wrote above to complete each of the following sentences.

4. Yukio built a small, homemade _____ aircraft.

5. He had to work _____ at his job to pay for the plane.

6. His plane looks old, but it is made of _____ materials.

7. Compared to _____ jets, Yukio's plane is very slow.

8. Yukio is careful not to _____ his small plane.

9. He wears aviator sunglasses for protection against _____ rays.

10. Yukio is proud of his abilities, but he is not _____ .

11. His friends think he is _____ , but Yukio likes to be safe.

Directions

Circle the prefix in each word.

oversleep	supermarket	overdue	ultraloyal
ultrafine	overtime	ultrafashionable	overlong
overjealous	overanxious	ultramodern	superhuman
overemotional	overheat	oversensitive	ultracritical

Directions

Write the word from the box that correctly matches each definition.

1. _____ very up-to-date

2. _____ too worried

3. _____ too emotional

4. _____ a large food store

5. _____ sleep too late

6. _____ finding too much fault

7. _____ greater than that of a normal person

8. _____ extra time beyond regular number of hours of work

9. _____ very high fashion

10. _____ too much wanting of what others have

11. _____ too easily affected by what others say or do

12. _____ lengthier than needed

13. _____ very fine

14. _____ past due

15. _____ very faithful

16. _____ heat too much

Name _____

▶ **Directions**

Add the prefix **trans** or **semi** to each base word or root below. The word you make should fit the definition.

Rule The prefix **trans** means *across, over,* or *beyond.* The prefix **semi** means *half* or *partly.*
transfer = to move from one place to another
transmit = to send across or pass along
semicircle = half a circle
semidark = partly dark

1. _____**portation:**
   a means of carrying something from one place
   to another

2. _____**mitting:** sending across or passing along

3. _____**skilled:** limited in training

4. _____**parent:** able to be seen through

5. _____**form:** to change the look or condition

6. _____**continental:** across a continent

7. _____**late:** to change into another form

▶ **Directions**

Write the words you made above to complete the sentences below.

8. Lasers _____ light into an even more valuable energy source.

9. Lasers use reflective glass (mirrors) and _____ glass to increase the strength of the laser beam.

10. The communications and _____ industries are two of many industries that rely on lasers.

11. A laser beam is capable of _____ a large number of television programs at the same time.

12. A laser can transmit transatlantic or
    _____ telephone calls
    very efficiently.

13. Compact discs use lasers to
    _____ computer
    information into music.

14. In the future, even _____ workers will use lasers.

Write the word from the box that correctly completes each sentence.

semidarkness	transported	semicircle	transaction	transient
transferred	Transcontinental	transit	semiskilled	transport

1. Stevie, Ray, Uncle Jed, and I sat in a _____ around the campfire.

2. In the _____ of evening, Uncle Jed began his story.

3. To _____ people and products across the country, the United States needed a railroad.

4. It was called the _____ Railroad.

5. The government and two railroad companies made a business

   _____ .

6. The government _____ land to the companies as an incentive.

7. The companies hired workers, including immigrants and _____ people.

8. Most of the workers were unskilled or _____ laborers.

9. The work was difficult, and supplies had to be _____ great distances, but finally the railroad was completed.

10. The railroad made _____ through the Great Plains safer and quicker.

Name _____

Directions

Rewrite each sentence. Use the correct word from the box to replace the phrase in boldface print.

Rule The prefix **sub** can mean *under, below,* or *not quite.* The prefix **mid** means *middle* or *the middle part.*

substandard = below the standard

midstream = the middle of the stream

submerge	midday	subfreezing	midnight
midwinter	submarine	subnormal	midway

1. It was **the middle of the day** when the captain received his orders.

_____

2. He changed course and headed his **ship that travels underwater** toward the open sea.

_____

_____

3. He gave the order to **go under water** and left his officers in charge.

_____

4. There were usually **below freezing** temperatures at this time of year.

_____

5. The water was always icy in **the middle of winter.**

_____

6. The temperatures this year, however, were **below normal.**

_____

7. At **twelve o'clock at night,** the captain gave the order to surface.

_____

8. The ship was **halfway** through its journey when it broke through the ice.

_____

_____

Read each sentence and fill in the circle under the word that best completes it. Write the answer on the line.

1. _____ vacations are the best.

Midsummer	Midriff	Midship
○	○	○

2. My cousin lives on a farm in the _____.

midair	Midwest	midstream
○	○	○

3. I left my home in the _____ for one month to visit him.

subside	submarine	suburbs
○	○	○

4. First I rode on the _____ to get to the airport.

midway	subway	subscribe
○	○	○

5. I was on a plane in _____ before I knew it.

midair	midtown	suburbs
○	○	○

6. I tightened the seat belt against my _____.

subway	midriff	midyear
○	○	○

7. Then I read a book with an interesting _____.

midstream	sublet	subplot
○	○	○

8. I fell asleep _____ through the flight.

midway	sublet	midland
○	○	○

9. A terrible storm had just _____ when I got to the farm.

subdued	substantial	subsided
○	○	○

10. The strong winds had _____.

subsurface	subdued	midpoint
○	○	○

11. A flooded creek had eroded the topsoil, exposing the _____.

midair	midriff	subsoil
○	○	○

12. At _____, the creek was six feet deep.

midlevel	subfloor	midstream
○	○	○

13. My cousin's hideout had become a _____ cave.

submarine	midland	subsoil
○	○	○

14. At _____, after the clouds were gone, we went outside to look at the stars.

midday	midnight	midriff
○	○	○

Name _____

 Directions

Use the words in the box to answer the questions.
Use each word only once.

Rule Uni, mono, bi, and tri are prefixes that show number. **Uni** and **mono** mean *one*. **Bi** means *two*. **Tri** means *three*.

unicorn	bilingual
monotonous	monotone
tricycle	triplets
biped	biplane
unicycle	monolingual

1. Which vehicle listed above has three wheels?

_____

2. Which word describes people who can speak two languages?

_____

3. What is the name of an imaginary animal that resembles a horse with one long horn in the center of its forehead?

_____

4. How could you describe a boring job in which you do one thing over and over again?

_____

5. What is another name for a two-footed animal?

_____

6. What are three babies born at the same time to one mother called?

_____

7. What do you call a flat speaking voice that uses just one dull tone?

_____

8. Which word describes someone who speaks only one language?

_____

9. What kind of plane has two sets of wings, one above the other?

_____

10. What is a one-wheeled vehicle that a circus clown might ride?

_____

Add the prefix **uni, mono, bi,** or **tri** to each base word or root. The word you make should fit the definition.

1. _____**pod:** a three-legged support

2. _____**forms:** distinctive clothes of a particular group

3. _____**son:** speaking the same words at one time

4. _____**lingual:** speaking two languages

5. _____**noculars:** eyepieces utilizing both eyes to see distant objects

6. _____**ennial:** happening every three years

7. _____**tonous:** having no variety

8. _____**cycle:** a two-wheeled vehicle

▶ **Directions**

Write a word you made above to complete each sentence.

9. Since the folk festival is _____ , Mr. Mulvey takes me every three years.

10. The festival is nearby, but we can't go by _____ because Mr. Mulvey brings a lot of equipment.

11. Mr. Mulvey is a photographer, so I help him by carrying his _____ .

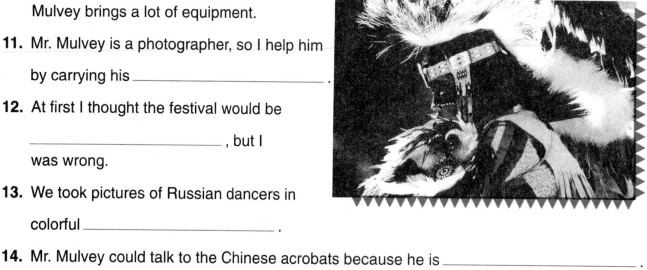

12. At first I thought the festival would be _____ , but I was wrong.

13. We took pictures of Russian dancers in colorful _____ .

14. Mr. Mulvey could talk to the Chinese acrobats because he is _____ .

15. A group of Native Americans performed a traditional chant in _____ .

16. The stage was so far away, I had to use _____ .

Name _____

Directions

Read the story. Circle each word that begins with one of the following prefixes: **sub, mid, trans, super, over, ultra, uni,** or **bi.** You will circle fourteen words.

It is twelve o'clock at night, and you are gazing into the clear, midwinter sky. The midnight stars have transformed the sky, creating an overwhelming brilliance. The universe beckons overhead as you survey it through your binoculars.

Stars have been a subject of wonder since ancient times. In fact, the study of the stars is rooted in superstition. Long ago, people imagined that the stars were united in groups to form pictures of people, animals, and objects in the sky. They made up many stories about these constellations, or "star pictures."

Today, because of ultramodern equipment, astronomers know much more about the night sky. They know that the constellations are not supernatural figures. Stars are huge balls of burning gases, many of which are much larger than our sun. Although stars are very large, they appear to be small, twinkling points of light. This is because they are so far away. The light from the stars is transmitted to us across millions and millions of miles. Satellites, optical and radio telescopes, and other instruments have helped astronomers measure the distance, motion, and substance of the stars. But the names ancient people gave to the constellations are still used today.

Directions

Choose a word from those you circled and write it by its definition.

1. _____ changed

2. _____ very modern

3. _____ middle of winter

4. _____ beyond normal

5. _____ middle of the night

6. _____ joined together as one

7. _____ everything in space

8. _____ above the head

9. _____ something being studied and looked at

10. _____ sent from place to place

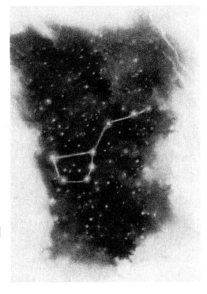

▶ **Directions**

Combine each pair of sentences below into one sentence, using a connecting word such as **and, so, but, because,** or **yet.** Remember that a comma is usually used before a connecting word, but a comma is *not* used before the word **because.**

1. If you watch the sky nightly, you will notice that the stars seem to move. It is really the earth that is moving.

   _____

   _____

2. Ancient people believed the earth was the center of the universe. Nicolaus Copernicus proposed that the earth moves around the sun.

   _____

   _____

3. Until this century, people thought only eight planets orbited the sun. In 1930 Clyde W. Tombaugh discovered Pluto.

   _____

   _____

4. It is nearly impossible for astronomers to experiment with the objects they study. They study them from great distances.

   _____

   _____

5. Optical telescopes measure the light that comes from stars. Radio telescopes measure radio waves that come from the sky.

   _____

   _____

Name _____

▶ Directions
Read the sentences and underline each word that contains the root **pos, pel,** or **pul.**

Definition A **root** is a word part to which prefixes and suffixes can be added to make new words. If you know the meanings of word parts, you can often figure out the meaning of a new word.

Rules The root **pos** usually means *put* or *place*. The roots **pel** and **pul** usually mean *push* or *drive*.
posture = the way one holds one's body
re**pel** = to drive back

1. Juanita composed a letter to her friends back home.
2. She wanted to dispel a rumor they had heard.
3. Somehow, word of her expulsion from school had reached them.
4. In fact, the opposite was true.
5. Juanita had not been expelled, but was doing very positive things.
6. She felt compelled to let them know the truth.
7. She deposited the letter in the mailbox.

▶ Directions
Write the letter of the correct definition next to each word.

_____ **8.** deposited
_____ **9.** expelled
_____ **10.** composed
_____ **11.** dispel
_____ **12.** expulsion
_____ **13.** positive
_____ **14.** opposite
_____ **15.** compelled

a. doing some good or helping in some way

b. the act of forcing out

c. to put something somewhere, often for safekeeping

d. made to do something

e. created or wrote

f. the reverse; something very different from

g. driven out; forced out

h. to drive away; to make disappear

Rules The root **port** means *carry.*
The root **ject** means *throw.*
porter = a person who carries things
e**ject** = to throw out

rejected	portable	imported	reports
important	eject	report	deportment

1. Carlos has an extremely _____ job at the electronics factory.

2. He inspects each piece of equipment, determining whether each will be

   sold or _____ .

3. He checks the various parts that have been _____ from other countries.

4. Carlos begins his inspections by checking the _____ televisions.

5. Carlos _____ his inspections to the video department.

6. He evaluates not only the video recorders, but the mechanisms that allow them to

   _____ a tape that has been viewed.

7. When Carlos completes his inspections, he writes a detailed _____ for his supervisor, Bob.

8. Bob has always been impressed with Carlos's excellent work and his fine

   _____ .

Directions

Match each word with its definition.

____ **9.** reject

____ **10.** deportment

____ **11.** portable

____ **12.** report

____ **13.** ejected

____ **14.** export

a. thrown out; forced out

b. conduct; behavior

c. to refuse to take or to throw away

d. a statement or account of something

e. able to be carried easily

f. to send goods to another country for sale

Name _____

▶ **Directions**

Read the sentences and underline each word that contains the root **aud** or **dict**.

Rules The root **dict** usually means *tell* or *say*. The root **aud** means *hear*.
dictate = to say with authority
audible = loud enough to be heard

1. The crew is working to create the audio portion of a commercial.
2. Abby, who will perform the voice-over, speaks with crisp diction.
3. At the audition, the commercial's director was impressed with her.
4. He knew Abby's pleasant voice would appeal to an audience.
5. Abby looked in her pocket dictionary for a word's pronunciation.
6. The director issued an edict to Abby and the crew: "Begin recording!"
7. When he played back the recording, it was barely audible.
8. "I predict we will find that something is wrong with our equipment," he said.

▶ **Directions**

Match each word with its definition.

_____ 9. audio

_____ 10. dictator

_____ 11. edict

_____ 12. audiotape

_____ 13. contradict

_____ 14. dictionary

_____ 15. predict

_____ 16. audience

a. a strong statement or command

b. a group of people who listen or watch

c. involving sound or hearing

d. a book containing definitions for words

e. a person whose commands must be obeyed

f. to forecast; to say ahead of time

g. a tape recording of sound

h. to deny; to say the opposite of

Directions

Complete each sentence with a word from the box.

capable	reception	accept	capacity	captured
receiving	acceptance	receipts	receptacle	captivating

1. Last night, we attended an elegant _____ .

2. The huge room was filled to _____ .

3. Carol Parks gave a speech to _____ the nomination for governor.

4. Everyone knows she is _____ of being a great governor.

5. An excellent speaker, Ms. Parks _____ the crowd's attention.

6. It was an especially _____ speech.

7. She asked that written suggestions be placed in a _____ .

8. She offered _____ to those who made contributions.

9. Today, the newspapers praised her _____ speech.

10. She has been _____ phone calls all day from people wishing her success.

Directions

Match each word with its definition.

_____ **11.** captives   **a.** to take something offered

_____ **12.** receive   **b.** a person in an office who greets people

_____ **13.** intercept   **c.** people taken prisoner

_____ **14.** receptacle   **d.** to seize something that is on its way from one place to another

_____ **15.** receptionist   **e.** a container

Name _____

▶ **Directions**

Ten words containing the roots **spec** or **spect** and **mit** or **miss** are hidden in the puzzle. Some of the words go across and some go down. Circle each word and write it on the line.

Rules The roots **spec** and **spect** mean *see, look,* or *examine.* The roots **mit** and **miss** mean *send* or *let go.*

    spectator = an onlooker
    dis**miss** = to send away

```
S  T  Q  A  D  M  I  T  I  R  S  P
U  P  E  B  N  K  N  I  U  P  F  E
B  P  H  S  I  N  S  P  E  C  T  R
M  A  S  R  C  H  P  B  D  Q  G  S
I  K  X  E  M  V  E  W  O  J  T  P
T  R  M  S  P  E  C  I  M  E  N  E
F  E  B  P  H  J  T  E  V  C  X  C
U  M  O  E  G  Z  O  M  I  T  V  T
Z  I  G  C  O  A  R  W  D  I  L  I
G  T  Y  T  A  W  R  V  F  J  D  V
Y  T  Y  R  N  L  C  K  N  Q  Y  E
D  I  S  M  I  S  S  A  L  M  Z  E
```

1. _____
2. _____
3. _____
4. _____
5. _____
6. _____
7. _____
8. _____
9. _____
10. _____

▶ **Directions**

Complete each sentence with a word from the puzzle.

11. I _____ that I was squeamish about the blood test at first.

12. From my _____ , it wasn't really fun.

13. I certainly _____ the nurse who drew the blood.

14. She said she would _____ the sample to the lab.

15. There, the _____ will be evaluated.

▶ **Directions**

Read each sentence and underline the word that has the root **man**.

> **Rule** The root **man** means *hand*.
>
> **man**ual = made or done by hand

1. My older brother, David, is the manager of Zippy's Video Arcade.
2. David has been managing the arcade for nearly two years.
3. Since he manipulates the controls quickly, David can win any video game he plays.
4. Some of the games are voice-activated, but I prefer those that are manual.
5. If I use my best manners, I can usually convince David to play a game with me.
6. We play Blast-Off, a game that allows us to maneuver astronauts on the screen.
7. In the game, a space ship is under the command of our astronauts.
8. Aliens have boarded the space ship and are demanding a lot of money.
9. The game's object is to keep the astronauts from being placed in manacles by the aliens.
10. I am working on the manuscript for a book of tips about winning the game.
11. When I am older, perhaps I'll manufacture my own video games.

▶ **Directions**

Write the letter of the correct word beside its definition.

_____ **12.** polite way of behaving

_____ **13.** handcuffs; objects to tie the hands together

_____ **14.** worked by hand, as a car transmission

_____ **15.** something written by hand

_____ **16.** fingernail and hand care

_____ **17.** to have charge of or direct

_____ **18.** to move something around skillfully

a. manipulate

b. manuscript

c. manners

d. manacles

e. manicure

f. manage

g. manual

Name _____

 Directions

Read the story. Use a word from the box to complete each unfinished sentence.

positive	predict	captured	compelled	manually	dictionary
deceive	submitted	manuscripts	adjective	rejected	portable
admit	portfolio	prospector	subject		

I have always wanted to be a writer. In fact, I often feel _____ to
                                                                                    1
write. I like to write about almost any _____, ranging from animals to
                                                              2

space travel. Sometimes I write _____, but other times I use my
                                              3

computer, which is small and _____. I carry a pocket
                                          4
_____ around with me so I can look up new and interesting words.
         5
Sometimes you need a good _____, like *horrendous* or *cunning,* to
                                         6

describe a noun.

Last year, I _____ one of my stories to a magazine, but it was
                          7
_____. I must _____ that I was disappointed,
         8   9
but I will try again. I _____ that I will be successful in the future.
                                    10
    I have a _____ of my work that I carry around. It has all my
                      11
_____. One of the best is a story about a
         12

_____ who is looking for gold in the 1800s.
         13
He is _____ he has found a big strike.
                    14
But it turns out that someone had hidden fake gold to

_____ him. I think I
         15

_____ the prospector's feelings of joy,
         16
disbelief, and anger quite well. Perhaps this is the next story I will
try to have published.

Read the paragraph. Underline the sentence that is the main idea. Then write the sentences that give supporting details. Draw a line through the sentence that does not give a supporting detail.

Hint · When you write a paragraph, all the information in it should tell about the same thing. One sentence should state the main idea. The other sentences should give supporting details.

Before I could play baseball, I had to submit to a complete physical checkup at the doctor's office. She checked my heart with a portable machine and inspected my ears and eyes. There were many magazines for people to read in the waiting room. The nurse gave me an injection for my hay fever. The doctor did not omit her lecture about eating well. When she dismissed me, the doctor predicted that I would be capable of having a good season as pitcher.

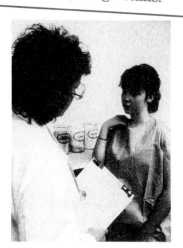

_____

_____

_____

_____

_____

_____

_____

_____

Directions

Now go back through the paragraph and circle each word that has a root that you have studied in this unit. Write the words on the line.

_____ _____ _____ _____

_____ _____ _____ _____

Name _____

> **Directions**
>
> Read the sentences and underline each compound word. Be sure that each word you underline is made up of two words that can stand on their own.

> **Definition** A compound word is made up of two or more other words. Each word can stand on its own and still have meaning.
> match + box = matchbox
> rattle + snake = rattlesnake

1. My grandparents live next to a famous lighthouse on the ocean.
2. Each year, for my birthday, we have a celebration at their house.
3. Since my birthday occurs in the summertime, we play outdoor games.
4. My sisters like to play baseball, but I prefer volleyball.
5. My grandfather and my mother, who is in a wheelchair, play chess outside.
6. They lean over the chessboard with great concentration.
7. Dad usually plays horseshoes with my grandmother.
8. Sometimes my dad, my sisters, and I go horseback riding at a nearby stable.
9. After sunset, we use a flashlight to try to signal the lighthouse.
10. Then, dressed in warm sweatshirts, we eat cupcakes and drink milk.

> **Directions**
>
> Choose the correct compound word from those you underlined and write it on the line beside its definition.

11. the parents of someone's father or mother _____

12. a portable electric light _____

13. small cakes _____

14. a chair mounted on wheels _____

15. heavy cotton shirts _____

> **Directions**

Choose a word from the box and write it on the line in front of the correct word to make a compound word.

water	thunder	row	hot	snow	air
pine	rain	box	hail	beef	steam

1. _____ boat   **2.** _____ car   **3.** _____ steak

4. _____ flakes   **5.** _____ cakes   **6.** _____ clap

7. _____ apple   **8.** _____ stones   **9.** _____ melon

10. _____ drops   **11.** _____ plane   **12.** _____ ship

> **Directions**

Write each compound word you made under the correct heading.

Food

13. _____

14. _____

15. _____

16. _____

Vehicles

17. _____

18. _____

19. _____

20. _____

Weather

21. _____

22. _____

23. _____

24. _____

> **Directions**

Choose words from the box. Use them to make compound words of your own, and write the words on the lines.

25. _____

26. _____

Name _____

▶ **Directions**

Read each group of words. If the words show that only one person or animal has something, write **one** on the first line. If the words show that more than one person or animal has something, write **more than one.** Then on the second line write the possessive form that can stand for each phrase.

Rule The possessive form is used to show that a person or an animal owns, has, or possesses something. To make a singular word show possession, usually add an apostrophe and an **s** (**'s**). If a word is plural and ends in **s,** just add an apostrophe.

Mike**'s** boat = a boat belonging to Mike
the dog**'s** feet = the feet belonging to the dog
girl**s'** uniforms = the uniforms belonging to the girls

1. the coat of Blair _____ _____

2. the snout of the seal _____ _____

3. the market of the farmers _____ _____

4. the owners of the dogs _____ _____

5. the nest of the owls _____ _____

6. the locker room of the boys _____ _____

7. the scores of the bowlers _____ _____

8. the skin of the snake _____ _____

9. the skateboard of Ellen _____ _____

10. the home of the zebras _____ _____

11. the kitchen of Mom _____ _____

12. the home of the muskrat _____ _____

Directions

Read each sentence. Write the correct possessive form of the word at the right.

Rules To make a word show possession: **1.** add **'s** to a singular word, **2.** add **'s** to a plural word not ending in **s**, **3.** add an apostrophe (') to a plural word ending in **s**.

> Bill**'s** house = a house belonging to Bill
> James**'s** portfolio = a portfolio belonging to James
> the children**'s** books = the books belonging to the children
> the bears**'** home = the home belonging to the bears

1. Our _____ curriculum includes computer skills.   (school)

2. It is our _____ turn to use the computer room today.   (class)

3. Ms. _____ class used the special room yesterday.   (Kinkaid)

4. All the _____ computer manuals must be distributed.   (students)

5. Mr. _____ computer is at the front of the class.   (Moss)

6. As he turns it on, the _____ green screen lights up.   (computer)

7. Then, the screen lights up on each _____ computer.   (student)

8. I hear the sound of _____ fingers on the keyboard.   (Kevin)

9. _____ word-processing skills are excellent.   (Chris)

10. The other _____ skills are not   (sixth-graders)
    quite as advanced.

11. After school, Tomás and I practice on his

    _____ computer.   (family)

12. We are welcome to use any of his _____ software.   (parents)

13. With _____ help, my abilities are improving.   (Tomás)

Name _____

▶ **Directions**

Choose one of the contractions below the line to complete each sentence. Then, on the line at the right, write the two words that form the contraction.

Definition A **contraction** is a word formed when two words are written together with one or more letters left out. An apostrophe is used in place of the missing letters.

is not = isn't (The letter **o** has been left out.)

you have = you've (The letters **ha** have been left out.)

1. Don, I wish _____ join my committee for the dance. (they've, you'd)

   _____

2. Barb originally said _____ help me in planning. (she'd, let's)

   _____

3. Since _____ busy with decorations, (she's, there's)

   she backed out.

   _____

4. I'm sure _____ be a real asset in planning! (you've, you'll)

   _____

5. _____ busy with the refreshment (He'll, Jerry's)

   committee.

   _____

6. Otherwise, _____ certain he would help us. (I'm, I'll)

   _____

7. Tonight's meeting _____ take too much time. (won't, hasn't)

   _____

8. It _____ take more than an hour. (should've, shouldn't)

   _____

9. _____ not going to be sorry you've (You're, You'll)

   agreed to help!

   _____

10. You _____ know how happy you've (should've, don't)

    made me!

    _____

▶ **Directions**

In the first column, write the two words the contraction stands for. In the second column, write the letter or letters that were left out.

	Words	**Letter or Letters Left Out**
1. aren't	_____	_____
2. Lee's	_____	_____
3. won't	_____	_____
4. they're	_____	_____
5. where's	_____	_____
6. she'll	_____	_____
7. we've	_____	_____
8. I'm	_____	_____
9. you'd	_____	_____
10. it's	_____	_____

▶ **Directions**

Underline the contraction in each sentence. Then write the two words it stands for.

11. Where's the movie section of the newspaper?   _____

12. Do you think that'll be enough money for the movie?   _____

13. I hope we're not too late to make it to the matinee.   _____

14. The movies at the East Cinema don't always start on time.   _____

15. We'd better hurry if we want to see this show!   _____

Name _____

- When a word has a prefix, divide the word between the prefix and the base word or the root. Some prefixes have more than one syllable.

- When a word has a suffix, divide the word between the suffix and the base word or the root. Some suffixes have more than one syllable.

- Sometimes a word has a prefix and a suffix with the base word or the root. If each word part has a vowel sound, then each part is a syllable.

- Divide a compound word between the words that make up the compound word. Then divide the smaller words into syllables if necessary.

▶ Directions

Write the number of vowel sounds you hear in each word. Write each word, then divide it into syllables using vertical lines.

1. compel   ____ _____
2. wallpaper   ____ _____
3. propose   ____ _____
4. rejected   ____ _____
5. icebreaker   ____ _____
6. yearbook   ____ _____
7. captivate   ____ _____
8. accept   ____ _____
9. submit   ____ _____
10. inspect   ____ _____
11. predictable ____ _____
12. posture   ____ _____
13. barefoot   ____ _____
14. admit   ____ _____
15. propulsion   ____ _____

16. battleship   ____ _____
17. deceiving   ____ _____
18. dismissal   ____ _____
19. imported   ____ _____
20. ringmaster   ____ _____
21. collarbone   ____ _____
22. oppose   ____ _____
23. contradict   ____ _____
24. intercept   ____ _____

▶ **Directions**

Read each sentence. Underline each two-syllable word. Circle each three-syllable word. Draw a box around each four-syllable word. Then write each word in the correct column, and use vertical lines to divide the words into syllables.

1. Our girls' basketball team made it to the championship tournament.

2. The team has played excellently during the winter season.

3. Playing forward, Beth has achieved an impressive record.

4. Beth is tall and dedicated, and she shoots accurately.

5. The team's co-captains, Susanna and Jo, have been outstanding this year.

6. Each game has attracted numerous cheering fans.

7. Last night's game was incredibly exciting.

8. Beth executed some complicated moves.

9. The outcome of the game was not predictable.

10. The score was surprisingly close.

Two Syllables	Three Syllables	Four Syllables

Name _____

downstairs	neighbor's	newspaper	Where's	bedroom
couldn't	homemade	he'd	bookcase	dog's

1. Even though _____ eaten earlier, Tod was hungry when he went to bed.

2. He crept _____ to see if there was any _____ blueberry pie left.

3. My _____ voice could wake the dead.

4. We can hear him as he bellows, "_____ the evening

_____?"

5. Ronnie _____ find his _____ leash.

6. He looked in his _____ and under the _____ .

 Directions

Choose one of the sentence pairs above. Write the main idea on the first line. Write the supporting detail on the second line. Now write two more sentences yourself to make a paragraph. Be sure your sentences support, or give more information about, the main idea. Include one contraction, one possessive, and one compound word in your sentences.

_____

_____

_____

_____

_____

_____

_____

_____

The following sentences are a mixed-up paragraph. Write them on the lines in the correct order to make a paragraph, with the main-idea sentence first. Circle each contraction, possessive, and compound word. Then write them on the lines below.

This means she's able to tell if two handwriting samples were written by the same person. Carla is a handwriting expert. You'll frequently find her on her way to the courthouse where she'll testify as an expert witness. Carla's ability is highly respected, and the police often seek her help in forgery cases. Carla claims that a person's writing is just as unique as a person's fingerprints.

_____

_____

_____

_____

_____

Contractions: _____

Possessives: _____

Compound words: _____

Name _____

Directions

Write the word that goes with each meaning. Circle the words you do not use.

Rule The suffixes **er** and **or** mean *something or someone that does something*. They can change a verb into a noun. The suffix **ist** also means *someone who does something*. But it changes one kind of noun into another kind of noun.

edit**or** = someone who edits
mix**er** = something that mixes
archaeolog**ist** = someone who knows the science of archaeology

photographer	optometrist	geologist	stretcher
juror	machinist	computer	farmer
customer	generator	organist	geology
machinery	collector	creator	organism

1. one who grows crops   _____

2. one who studies rocks   _____

3. one who takes pictures   _____

4. something that produces electricity   _____

5. something that works quickly with numbers and facts   _____

6. one who serves on a jury   _____

7. one who plays a musical instrument   _____

8. one who shops for goods   _____

9. one who works with machines   _____

10. one who makes something   _____

11. something that can be used to carry a person   _____

12. one who gathers large numbers of similar items   _____

13. one who tests vision and prescribes glasses   _____

There are 18 words hidden in the puzzle that have the suffixes **er, or,** or **ist.** Some of the words go across, and some go down. Circle each word as you find it, and write it in the correct column.

```
C D I V E R S O L O I S T
Z M K I R E A L I S T G Y
A I R S T A U R T V G A P
X N B I A N C E S T O R I
N E C T N I B C U B V C S
O R T O U R I S T M E O T
V L S R T R A I N E R M B
E A R T I S T P S E N P A
L O E A C T O R T R O U T
I D O C T O R W Y H R T T
S E S C A L A T O R U E E
T C D G F E S K A T E R R
```

er	or	ist
_____	_____	_____
_____	_____	_____
_____	_____	_____
_____	_____	_____
_____	_____	_____
_____	_____	_____

Now write the correct word from the puzzle beside its definition.

1. a moving stairway that carries people up or down _____

2. one who travels _____

3. one who teaches animals to do tricks _____

Name _____

▶ Directions

Add **er** or **est** to the base word you see below the line. Remember that when the base word ends in **e**, drop the **e** before adding **er** or **est**. If the base word ends in **y**, change the **y** to **i** before adding **er** or **est**.

Rule The suffix **er** is used to compare two objects or people. The suffix **est** is used to compare more than two objects or people.
Kim is tall**er** than Jo, but Peg is the tall**est** of all.

1. *Laugh It Up* is by far the _____ book I ever read.
   (great)

2. Willie is the book's hero, and he is the _____ character in it.
   (silly)

3. He is surely _____ than the character Anna, who never smiles.
   (funny)

4. In the story, Anna is several years _____ than Willie.
   (young)

5. Despite her youth, Anna is the _____ character in the book.
   (weary)

6. Willie decides to make Anna the _____ person in the world.
   (happy)

7. He devises funny stunts to make her _____ than she's ever been.
   (happy)

8. Each of Willie's stunts is _____ than the last!
   (tricky)

9. Finally, Anna smiles the _____ grin Willie has ever seen.
   (wide)

Look at the base word in boldface print. Then read each short paragraph. Use the base word or the base word plus the suffix **er** or **est** to complete each unfinished sentence. You may use a word twice.

1. busy

The _____ highway was the scene of many traffic jams. The

_____ corner was Randle and Foote Streets. Even on Sundays this corner

is _____ than any other.

2. bright

That star is the _____ one in the sky. It is _____ than

the one close to it, which is also a very _____ star.

3. wet

George gets _____ in a rainstorm than anyone I know. He doesn't carry

an umbrella. He says he's afraid it will get _____.

4. happy

Hannah always seems to be _____. She is _____

than her brother Hal. I wonder what she's so _____ about.

5. high

Connie can jump _____ than Alice. She can jump the

_____ of anyone on the track team. Everyone on the team can jump

_____ than I can.

6. long

The new trail to the top of the mountain was _____. Maybe it seemed

_____ than the old one because we were so hungry. It really seemed like

the _____ trail we had ever hiked.

Name _____

 Directions

Read each sentence and look at the word below the line. Form an adjective using the suffix **ous** or **al.** If the base word ends in **y,** change the **y** to **i** before adding the suffix. If it ends in **f,** usually change the **f** to **v** before adding the suffix.

Rule The suffix **ous** means *like, full of,* or *having.* The suffix **al** means *like* or *having to do with.* Both suffixes can change a noun into an adjective.

courage**ous** = full of courage
comic**al** = having to do with comedy

1. The house at the end of the block is a _____ monument.
(historic)

2. Miriam conducts _____ tours through the house.
(education)

3. She leads her tour groups through its _____ rooms.
(glory)

4. Miriam points out the _____ woodwork in the house.
(ornament)

5. She explains how the _____ furniture was created.
(tradition)

6. Miriam discusses the lives of the home's _____ owners.
(colony)

7. She shares many _____ stories with her groups.
(humor)

8. Some of the owners' antics were really quite _____ .
(comic)

9. Of course, life during colonial times could be _____ .
(danger)

10. When Miriam feels _____ , she says the house is haunted.
(mischief)

Read the words in the box. Then use the clues at the bottom of the page to complete the crossword puzzle.

sentimental	poisonous	mysterious	ornamental	fallacious
nervous	national	natural	famous	mountainous

Across
1. having to do with a country
6. full of mystery
7. having a reputation; being well-known
8. full of feeling
9. mistaken

Down
1. being tense
2. having to do with nature
3. full of harmful substances
4. having many mountains
5. for decoration

Name  _____

▶ **Directions**

Read the sentences and underline each word with the suffix **ward, en,** or **ize.** Then write each word you underlined in the correct column.

Rules The suffix **ward** means *toward* or *in the direction of.* It can change a noun into an adjective or adverb. The suffix **en** means *to make, to become,* or *made of.* It can change a noun into a verb or an adjective. The suffix **ize** means *to make* or *to become.* It can change a noun into a verb.

home**ward** = toward home
wood**en** = made of wood
legal**ize** = to make legal

1. I did not realize that going out in the boat would frighten you.
2. I apologize for assuming that you would want to go seaward with us.
3. You can watch from the shore as we loosen the ropes and go forward.
4. Before we get into the boat, we always make sure to fasten our life jackets.
5. Gregory kicks off from the shore with a backward push.
6. I look skyward to make sure the weather is good.
7. When we are on the boat, we all like to sing and harmonize loudly.
8. We like to modernize old songs.
9. When the days begin to shorten, we don't stay in the boat very long.

en	ward	ize
_____	_____	_____
_____	_____	_____
_____	_____	_____
_____	_____	_____

Complete each sentence by adding **ward, en,** or **ize** to each base word below the line.

1. This delay on the ground will certainly _____ our travel time.
   (length)

2. I had hoped that the clear skies and strong wind would _____ it.
   (short)

3. Does it _____ you to wait motionless on the ground for so long?
   (sad)

4. It was nice of the pilot to _____ for the long delay.
   (apology)

5. The flight attendant asks us to look _____ as he demonstrates
   safety procedures.
   (for)

6. Make sure Danny is not looking _____ during the demonstration.
   (back)

7. The flight attendants _____ the information they present.
   (standard)

8. The airplane finally finishes taxiing down the runway and moves

   _____ .
   (sky)

9. Its gleaming silver nose points _____ .
   (up)

10. As we soar into the sky, my spirits begin to _____ .
    (light)

11. Now I can _____ my dream of a vacation.
    (real)

12. Danny and I look _____ at the landscape.
    (down)

13. Hardly a word is _____ as we gaze at the scenery below.
    (spoke)

Name _____

▶ **Directions**

Complete each sentence by adding **ful** or **ness** to each base word below the line.

Rules The suffix **ful** can mean *full of* or *having a tendency to be*. It can also mean a *certain amount*. When the suffix **ful** is added to a noun, it changes the word either into an adjective or into a different noun. The suffix **ness** means *quality* or *condition of being*. It changes adjectives into nouns.

joy**ful** = full of joy

spoon**ful** = an amount that fills a spoon

sweet**ness** = the quality of being sweet

1. Marta is a hairdresser with very

_____ hands.
(skill)

2. She is always serious and

_____ about her work.
(care)

3. Without such skill, the results can be _____!
(dread)

4. I have had many haircuts that left me _____ .
(tear)

5. My hair is hard to manage because of its _____ .
(thick)

6. I am _____ that Marta can tame this wild mane!
(hope)

7. Marta fills me with _____ when she cuts my hair.
(glad)

8. She is always _____ when offering styling tips.
(truth)

9. I am _____ to have her as my hairdresser.
(thank)

10. Marta can count on me to be a _____ customer.
(faith)

▶ Directions

There are 12 words containing the suffixes **ful** or **ness** hidden in the puzzle. Some of the words go across and some go down. Circle each word as you find it, and write it in the correct column.

ful

_____

_____

_____

_____

_____

_____

ness

_____

_____

_____

_____

_____

_____

```
B  C  F  G  H  J  B  L  D  R  S  D
H  A  R  M  F  U  L  A  X  Y  T  A
S  R  B  N  G  C  A  F  Y  Z  R  M
Z  E  A  S  N  D  C  D  P  Q  I  P
P  F  G  T  M  X  K  L  M  R  C  N
W  U  F  N  E  W  N  E  S  S  T  E
G  L  U  D  F  G  E  H  K  M  N  S
T  D  L  P  H  T  S  N  I  T  E  S
F  I  T  N  E  S  S  O  L  V  S  T
T  F  O  C  R  Z  P  R  L  W  S  L
Q  J  B  F  P  A  I  L  F  U  L  B
B  H  E  A  L  T  H  F  U  L  D  C
D  A  R  K  N  E  S  S  L  M  N  P
```

▶ Directions

Write a word from the puzzle to complete each sentence.

1. Jack is very _____ about maintaining his good health.

2. He exercises every day to improve his physical _____ .

3. Jack always eats _____ food so his body will be strong.

4. He would never do anything that would be _____ to his body.

Name _____

▶ **Directions**

Each word in the box has a suffix you studied in this unit. First read the editorial and then write the word from the box that best completes each sentence. The suffix below each line will help you choose the correct word. You will not use all the words in the box.

additional	sideward	furious	sympathize	mechanical	dangerous	peaceful
generalize	Arsonists	forward	brightness	greatness	organists	numerous
firefighters	drivers	frightful	stiffen	shorten	inspector	creator

Our town has seen some _____ events during the last weeks.
                                1 (ful)

_____ have burned down _____ buildings. We
        2 (ist)   3 (ous)

must _____ the punishment for this kind of crime. Arson is both
        4 (en)

_____ to people and a threat to business. As an
        5 (ous)

_____ worry, the chief fire _____ says it is also a
        6 (al)   7 (or)

danger to the _____ whose job it is to put out the fires.
                    8 (er)

As a city, we must not be discouraged by the _____ of the problem.
                                                    9 (ness)

We must move _____ to solve it. Meanwhile, we _____
              10 (ward)   11 (ize)

with anyone who has lost a home or business.

▶ **Directions**

Read the statements. Put a check in front of each statement that is a paraphrase of the editorial. Put an X in front of each one that is not a paraphrase of what the editorial says.

_____ **1.** Arson is a terrible crime.

_____ **2.** Arsonists should live somewhere out of the city.

_____ **3.** Firefighters should have safer equipment.

_____ **4.** The penalty for arson should be increased.

_____ **5.** The city should move to fight arson.

_____ **6.** The chief inspector should be replaced.

Think about the things you read, see, or hear during any one week. Many of these things try to persuade or convince you to think or act in a certain way. Read the examples below. Circle each one that is written to convince or persuade. Draw a line through each one that is not.

1. an advertisement for soap that tells you people will love you if you use it
2. a funny TV comedy show
3. an editorial that calls for citizens to vote in the next election
4. a news story about an event in China
5. a radio program that plays music
6. a letter from a cousin asking you to come and visit
7. a poster that tries to get people to join the Army
8. a set of directions telling how to make a model plane

▶ **Directions**

Write three or more sentences to convince someone to act or think in a certain way. You may write an editorial for the school paper or an advertisement for something you want to sell. Use at least five words that have the following suffixes.

er	or	ist	er	est	ous	al	ward	en	ize	ful	ness

_____

_____

_____

_____

_____

_____

Name _____

▶ **Directions**

Fill in the circle under the word that correctly completes each sentence.

Rules The suffix **hood** means *state or condition of being.* The suffix **ship** means *state of, rank of,* or *art of something.* The suffix **ment** means *act of* or *state of something.* Each of these suffixes can change one noun into another noun.

mother**hood** = the condition of being a mother
governor**ship** = the rank of governor
improve**ment** = the act of improving

1. Sara and Joan share a special ____.

friendship ○   courtship ○   falsehood ○

2. They grew up in the same ____.

motherhood ○   authorship ○   neighborhood ○

3. They tell stories about their ____.

enrollment ○   childhood ○   likelihood ○

4. They recall one story with great ____.

authorship ○   enjoyment ○   adulthood ○

5. The girls had a shared ____—measles.

friendship ○   ailment ○   kinship ○

6. Suffering through it was a ____.

falsehood ○   placement ○   hardship ○

7. The experience created a special ____.

governorship ○   kinship ○   statement ○

8. Sara has never had an ____ with Joan.

argument ○   authorship ○   amendment ○

9. Joan has never told Sara a ____.

brotherhood ○   falsehood ○   astonishment ○

10. Many people view the girls with ____.

amendment ○   childhood ○   astonishment ○

11. They marvel at this incredible ____.

livelihood ○   partnership ○   craftsmanship ○

12. Some even envy the girls' ____.

ailment ○   improvement ○   relationship ○

13. The girls will be friends through ____.

adulthood ○   scholarship ○   statehood ○

14. They have a ____ to each other.

commitment ○   womanhood ○   championship ○

▶ **Directions**

Circle the word that correctly completes each analogy. Then write the word on the line.

Definition An **analogy** compares things that are alike in some ways. Some analogies show how pairs of things are alike.

Light is to **dark** as **slow** is to **fast**.

1. **Up** is to **down** as **truth** is to _____ .
   neighborhood   falsehood   statehood

2. **Argument** is to **quarrel** as **settlement** is to _____ .
   agreement   equipment   ailment

3. **Handwriting** is to **penmanship** as **studying** is to _____ .
   partnership   friendship   scholarship

4. **Tourist** is to **traveler** as **community** is to _____ .
   installment   neighborhood   championship

5. **Sweet** is to **sour** as **adulthood** is to _____ .
   falsehood   likelihood   childhood

6. **Wood** is to **house** as **cement** is to _____ .
   measurement   enlargement   pavement

7. **Baseball** is to **game** as **World Series** is to _____ .
   kinship   championship   authorship

8. **Date** is to **appointment** as **sickness** is to _____ .
   payment   retirement   ailment

9. **Stop** is to **go** as **boredom** is to _____ .
   excitement   enrollment   engagement

10. **Change** is to **improvement** as **fix** is to _____ .
    assignment   adjustment   advancement

Name _____

Directions

Circle the base word in each word in boldface print. Then use the base word and the **suffix** in parentheses to form the word that will complete each sentence.

Rule The suffixes **able** and **ible** mean *able to be*. The suffix **able** can also mean *full of*. These suffixes can change a noun or a verb into an adjective.

break**able** = able to be broken
digest**ible** = able to be digested
charit**able** = full of charity

1. Something that can be **r e p a i r e d** is _____ . (able)

2. Something that can be **r e v e r s e d** is _____ . (ible)

3. Something that you **l i k e d** was _____ . (able)

4. Something that can be **r e p r o d u c e d** is _____ . (ible)

5. Something that can be **i n s u r e d** is _____ . (able)

6. Something that can be **c o n v e r t e d** is _____ . (ible)

7. Something that can be **d e d u c t e d** is _____ . (ible)

8. Something that can be **e n j o y e d** is _____ . (able)

Directions

Now use one of the words you wrote to complete each sentence.

9. My brother Joe bought a car with a soft, _____ top.

10. The car needs some work, but Joe believes it is _____ .

11. When Joe drives with the top down, he wears his _____ jacket.

12. He always has an _____ time in his car!

Read the base words in the box. Use each base word and suffix to form a new word that will complete one of the sentences. If the base word ends in **e,** drop the **e** before adding a suffix beginning with a vowel.

break (able)	flex (ible)	read (able)	enjoy (able)
disagree (able)	wear (able)	favor (able)	response (ible)
play (able)	excite (able)	inflate (able)	convert (ible)

1. Tammy is happy that her baby-sitting job is quite _____ .

2. She works for the Manns, who find her extremely trustworthy and

   _____ .

3. Tammy works each weekend, but her hours are _____ .

4. The two children enjoy Tammy's company because she is never

   _____ .

5. The children are _____ , but Tammy can calm them down.

6. Tammy never allows them to play with anything _____ .

7. She helps them practice their printing so it will be _____ .

8. She helps them take care of their clothes so they will be _____ .

9. They listen to records so old that they are barely _____ .

10. Tammy takes the children outside when weather conditions are

    _____ .

11. When the children play in the pool, Tammy floats on an _____ raft.

12. The Manns drive Tammy home in their _____ .

Name _____

 Directions

Read the words in the box. Notice that there is a noun and a verb in each pair. Choose the word that best completes each definition.

Rule The suffixes **ion**, **ation**, and **ition** usually mean *the act of* or *a condition of being*. Each of these suffixes can change a verb into a noun.

connect**ion** = the condition of being connected

present**ation** = the act of presenting

add**ition** = the condition of being added

tax, taxation	relate, relation	locate, location	admire, admiration
obstruct, obstruction	erupt, eruption	select, selection	reject, rejection
	compose, composition		

1. to create or to write something

   _____

2. the act of adding to the price of something by the government

   _____

3. a sudden burst of lava and rock from a volcano

   _____

4. a place

   _____

5. a large barrier or thing that blocks

   _____

6. to think well of, respect

   _____

7. the choosing of something

   _____

8. to refuse or not accept

   _____

9. any family member

   _____

Add a word from the box to the suffix below the line to complete each sentence. If the base word ends in **e,** drop the **e** before adding it to the suffix.

expect	vibrate	destruct	converse	present
add	combine	locate	inform	populate

1. Our Midwestern _____ makes us a prime target for tornadoes.
   (ion)

2. Yesterday we waited in nervous _____ of a fierce tornado's arrival.
   (ation)

3. Its _____ of speed and whirling air made it a menace.
   (ation)

4. It had struck a nearby town, creating widespread _____ .
   (ion)

5. Thankfully, no one of the town's _____ was injured.
   (ion)

6. In the basement, we could feel the _____ of the winds.
   (ion)

7. We kept the radio on, listening attentively for further _____ .
   (ation)

8. News broadcasts included the _____ of safety procedure stories.
   (ition)

9. We felt too anxious to engage in any _____ .
   (ation)

10. We cheered as a news _____ finally stated that the tornado had
    bypassed us.   (ation)

Name _____

Rule The suffixes **ance** and **ence** usually mean the *state of being* or *quality*. These suffixes can change a verb into a noun.

clear**ance** = the state of being cleared
depend**ence** = the quality of being dependent

persistence	confidence	dependence	clearance
alliance	competence	admittance	attendance

1. Benjamin and Susan were worried that _____ at the dance would be low.

2. They felt the suggested _____ fee was too high.

3. They formed an _____ to solve the problem.

4. By working together, they increased their _____ in each other.

5. They decided that using local sponsors could decrease the school's

   _____ on the fee.

6. They got _____ from the class advisor to act on their idea.

7. They sought sponsors with a great deal of business _____.

8. They were proud of the _____ they had shown in solving the problem.

WE WOULD LIKE TO THANK THE FOLLOWING SPONSORS OF THE DANCE:

MOM'S BAKERY

DOLE'S HARDWARE

CAROL'S COFFEE SHOP

Rules The suffix **ity** can mean the *quality, condition,* or *fact of being.* This suffix can change an adjective into a noun. The suffix **ive** means *likely to* or *having to do with.* It can change a verb into an adjective.

sincer**ity** = the quality of being sincere
impres**sive** = likely to impress

active	oddity	creative	objectivity
impressive	maturity	productive	automotive

1. Roger knew that planning for a career well ahead of time was a sign of

_____ .

2. He thought about what kind of job he wanted with a great deal of

_____ .

3. He did not want to sit at a desk—he wanted to be _____ .

4. Also, problem-solving appealed to his _____ side.

5. He considered becoming an _____ mechanic.

6. He had always been interested in cars, so this wouldn't be an _____ .

7. With this type of work he could be creative *and* _____ .

8. Roger's parents thought his planning was very _____ .

Name _____

 Directions

Use the words in the box to complete the letter.

allowance	neighborhood	application	education	retirement	enjoyable
population	advertisement	impressive	vacation	university	information

Dear Ray,

How do you like your new home and _____? I found

_____ in my encyclopedia that says the
2

_____ of your new city is 150,000.
3

I have a story to tell you. I think you will find it _____ and smile
4

over it. I saw an _____ in the newspaper for a job at the zoo. You
5

know I've been looking for a job because I need more money than my weekly

_____ pays me. So I filled out an _____
6   7

for the job. When I went in for an interview, they said they didn't pay very much. Do you know

why? It's because they have an excellent _____ program with lots
8

of benefits. Since I'm only sixteen, I'm not thinking about retirement right now; however, I may
take the job anyway if they offer it to me.

I hope you will think about coming back here for your _____
9

after high school. We could go to the _____ together. They have
10

very _____ courses in medicine.
11

See you during summer _____.
12

Your friend,
Dana

► **Directions**

Read each statement. Each one could be the first sentence in an article written to persuade. Choose one of the sentences and write a short paragraph made up of three or four sentences to persuade someone to do something. In your sentences, use words that have the suffixes **hood, ship, ment, ance, ence, ity, ive, able, ible, ion, ation,** or **ition.**

1. There are three good reasons why you should have a membership in the math club.
2. It would be a great idea to take Mrs. Clark's class in communication skills.
3. Our bicycle tune-up is just what you need—here's why!
4. Selling our T-shirts to your friends can be a profitable business for you.

_____

_____

_____

_____

_____

_____

_____

_____

► **Directions**

Now write the words from your sentences that contain any of the suffixes listed in the directions at the top.

_____

_____

_____

_____

_____

_____

_____

Name _____

 Directions

Read the words. Then make new words by adding the suffix above each column.

Rule When a short-vowel word ends in a single consonant, the consonant is usually doubled before adding a suffix that begins with a vowel.

jog + **ing** = jog**ging**

	er	ed	ing
1. trap	_____	_____	_____
2. drum	_____	_____	_____
3. blot	_____	_____	_____
4. chop	_____	_____	_____
5. bat	_____	_____	_____
6. ship	_____	_____	_____

 Directions

Read the words in the box and circle their base words. Then choose two words from the box to complete each sentence.

swimmers	batter	joggers	sitting	sunny	clapping
stopped	letting	running	getting	wettest	scanning

7. Yesterday was the _____ day of the year, but the rain finally

_____ .

8. Today people are _____ themselves enjoy the _____ weather.

9. At the track, _____ are _____ some exercise.

10. The lifeguard at the pool is _____ the _____ .

11. At the baseball game, the _____ is _____ toward second base.

12. The people _____ in the bleachers are _____ .

Circle each base word that ends in a single consonant. Then form new words by putting the base words and suffixes together. Write the words on the lines.

1. slip _____ er _____ ing _____ ed

2. bag _____ er _____ age _____ ed

3. glad _____ ly _____ ness _____ est

4. scrub _____ er _____ ing _____ ed

5. big _____ er _____ est _____ ness

6. jog _____ er _____ ed _____ ing

7. slim _____ ing _____ er _____ est

8. arm _____ ful _____ ed _____ ing

9. mad _____ en _____ er _____ ness

10. pack _____ ed _____ ing _____ er

11. ship _____ ers _____ ed _____ ing

12. fit _____ er _____ ful _____ ing

13. can _____ ed _____ ing _____ er

14. rent _____ er _____ ed _____ ing

15. rip _____ ed _____ ing _____ er

16. flap _____ ing _____ ed _____ er

17. chill _____ y _____ ing _____ ed

18. sharp _____ er _____ en _____ ness

19. map _____ ed _____ ing _____ s

20. clean _____ er _____ est _____ ing

21. drop _____ ing _____ ed _____ er

22. wild _____ ly _____ er _____ est

23. flat _____ er _____ est _____ en

24. fog _____ ed _____ ing _____ y

25. slug _____ ing _____ er _____ ed

Lesson 63: Words that double the final consonant to add a suffix

Name _____

⟩ **Directions**

Form new words by adding the suffixes.

Rule When a word ends in a final **e**, usually the **e** is dropped before adding a suffix that begins with a vowel. Usually the **e** is not dropped when adding a suffix that begins with a consonant.
change + **ing** = chang**ing**

1. migrate + ion _____

2. divide + er _____

3. grave + est _____

4. dance + ing _____

5. polite + ness _____

6. ripe + ness _____

7. hesitate + ion _____

8. secure + ly _____

9. wrinkle + ed _____

10. believe + able _____

⟩ **Directions**

Read each sentence. Circle each word that drops the final **e** to add a suffix. Then write the base word of each circled word on the lines.

11. The latest grade Gary received in math wasn't very good.

12. He decided it was desirable to work harder.

13. He hoped to do better and believed he could do it.

14. Everyone was amazed at his determination.

15. Mr. Martin, his teacher, praised him as he improved.

16. Gary derived great pleasure from his continued success.

_____   _____

_____   _____

_____   _____

_____   _____

_____   _____

▶ Directions

Form new words by adding suffixes. Remember, usually the final **e** is dropped if the suffix begins with a vowel.

1. startle + ing _____
2. have + ing _____
3. mobile + ity _____
4. elevate + or _____
5. write + ing _____
6. blue + est _____
7. compute + er _____
8. sincere + ly _____
9. hope + ful _____
10. appreciate + ed _____
11. decide + ed _____
12. describe + able _____
13. practice + ed _____
14. improve + ment _____
15. forgive + ness _____
16. guide + ance _____

▶ Directions

Complete each sentence with one of the words you wrote.

17. Sarah helped Sue learn to use her new _____.

18. Sue wanted to use it for _____ school papers.

19. She _____ Sarah's help and wanted to do something for her in return.

20. She knew Sarah played softball but was _____ trouble with her hitting.

21. If Sarah could show an _____, she might make the team.

22. Sue was the team's best hitter, so she _____ to help Sarah.

23. She was _____ that Sarah could do it.

24. The two girls _____ together every day.

25. With Sue's _____, Sarah worked hard and made the team.

Name _____

For each word, underline the first suffix and draw a circle around the second suffix. Remember, **s** can be a suffix.

Rule Many words have more than one suffix. Additional suffixes are added according to the rules you have learned.

1. h a r d e n e d
2. f o o l i s h n e s s
3. v a c a t i o n s
4. f e a r f u l n e s s
5. t e a r f u l l y
6. c o u r a g e o u s l y
7. l e g a l i z e d
8. t h o u g h t f u l l y
9. p e a c e f u l n e s s
10. a d o p t i o n s
11. a c t i o n s
12. m o i s t e n e d

 Directions

Read each sentence. Fill in the circle beside the word with more than one suffix that completes the sentence. Then write the base words on the lines below.

13. When Carla ____, she found a beautiful package on the edge of her bed.
  ○ stretched ○ awakened ○ looked

14. Carla looked at the package ____.
  ○ seriously ○ curiously ○ expectantly

15. She opened it very ____.
  ○ cautiously ○ carefully ○ easily

16. Carla didn't want to ____ break anything.
  ○ suddenly ○ accidentally ○ horribly

17. Seeing the gift, she was ____ surprised.
  ○ happiness ○ delightfully ○ excited

18. ____, it was exactly what she had been wishing for.
  ○ Amazingly ○ Surely ○ Certainly

19. ____, Grandma had known what she wanted.
  ○ Somehow ○ Mysteriously ○ Exactly

20. Carla thanked Grandma for her ____.
  ○ thoughtfulness ○ generosity ○ kindness

21. _____
22. _____
23. _____
24. _____
25. _____
26. _____
27. _____
28. _____

Directions

Combine each base word with the two suffixes.

1. thought + ful + ness _____
2. sharp + en + ed _____
3. awake + en + ed _____
4. fear + ful + ness _____
5. truth + ful + ness _____
6. celebrate + ion + s _____
7. amaze + ing + ly _____
8. power + less + ness _____
9. thank + ful + ness _____
10. cheer + ful + ly _____
11. wide + en + ing _____
12. favor + able + ly _____
13. fright + en + ing _____
14. hope + ful + ly _____

Directions

Use the words you wrote to complete the following sentences.

15. A person who never lies or cheats has the virtue of

    _____ .

16. A synonym for *happily* is

    _____ .

17. An antonym of *powerfulness* is

    _____ .

18. The alarm clock _____ everyone at six o'clock this morning.

19. A synonym for *scary* is

    _____ .

20. A pencil with a broken point needs to be

    _____ .

21. The traffic had to follow a detour because the road crews were _____ the street.

22. There were many _____ in our town when the high school football team won the championship.

23. Someone who is afraid is in a state of _____ .

24. To be in agreement with something means to react _____ to it.

Name _____

 Directions

Study the examples. Then complete the rules for adding suffixes to words ending in **y**.

Forming Plurals		Adding Other Suffixes	
study—studies	valley—valleys	funny—funnier	occupy—occupying
story—stories	bay—bays	heavy—heaviest	obey—obeyed

1. If a word ends in **y** preceded by a consonant, make it plural by changing the **y** to _____

   and adding the letters _____ .

2. If a word ends in **y** preceded by a vowel, make it plural by adding _____ .

3. If a word ends in **y** preceded by a consonant, change the letter _____ to _____ before
   adding any suffix except **ing.**

4. If a word ends in **y** preceded by a _____ , just add the suffix.

 Directions

Combine each base word and suffix. Then write the new word to complete each sentence.

5. Mike and Jeff went to the carnival and (stay + ed) _____ until
   closing time.

6. Mike went on more rides than Jeff, so he felt (dizzy + er) _____ .

7. They both agreed that a new ride, The Tornado, was the (scary + est)

   _____ .

8. They (try + ed) _____ their luck at the games and won some prizes.

9. Mike and Jeff both had a very (enjoy + able) _____ time.

10. There were so many (activity + s) _____ , they wished they could
    stay longer.

11. They made plans to return in a few

    (day + s) _____

Make new words by adding the suffixes.

1. spy + es _____
2. occupy + es _____
3. pry + ed _____
4. canary + es _____
5. lazy + er _____
6. healthy + est _____
7. sky + es _____
8. turkey + s _____
9. bossy + er _____
10. study + ed _____
11. sentry + es _____
12. dirty + er _____

▶ **Directions**

Use the words you wrote to complete the crossword puzzle.

Across
2. tried to learn
4. lives in
6. guards
9. more covered with grime than another
10. large birds that are eaten by many people on Thanksgiving Day

Down
1. having the best health of all
2. people who keep secret watch on the action of others
3. more fond of telling others what to do than another
5. small yellow birds that sing sweetly
7. the heavens
8. raised, moved, or forced with a lever

Name _____

heavy + ly = heavily	wobble + ly = wobbly
cheery + ly = cheerily	feeble + ly = feebly

1. When a word ends in **y** preceded by a consonant, follow this rule to add the suffix **ly**:

   Change the letter _____ to _____ before adding **ly**.

2. When a word ends in **le,** follow this rule to add the suffix **ly**:

   Drop the letters _____ and add **ly**.

 Directions

Add the suffix **ly** to each word. Then complete the sentences using words you formed.

3. easy _____ **4.** possible _____ **5.** lucky _____

6. simple _____ **7.** happy _____ **8.** noble _____

9. bubble _____ **10.** hearty _____ **11.** hasty _____

12. sleepy _____ **13.** thrifty _____ **14.** wiggle _____

15. Jenny wasn't fully awake yet, so she _____ got out of bed.

16. She realized she had overslept and _____ tried to get ready.

17. She couldn't _____ be late for school today.

18. The spelling bee would be the first activity,

   and she _____ had to be there.

19. _____ the school bus was a little late, so she caught it in time.

20. Jenny is such a good speller that she

   _____ won the spelling bee.

21. She smiled _____ , glad that she had been on time.

Choose a word from the box that fits each clue and write it on the line. Then circle each word you wrote in the puzzle below. Some of the words in the puzzle go across, and others go down.

heavily	wobbly	simply	greedily	ably	busily
prickly	saucily	pebbly	easily	sleepily	happily
nimbly	weepily	sparkly	sloppily	crackly	nobly
angrily	drizzly	dizzily	feebly	lazily	wiggly

1. _____ in an angry way

2. _____ weather that is damp and misty

3. _____ the way an ocean beach filled with small stones looks

4. _____ in a lazy way

5. _____ in a busy way

6. _____ like a chair that would move from side to side if you sat on it

7. _____ how fireworks look

8. _____ how fire sounds

9. _____ in a greedy way

```
A N B R G W O B B L Y D E R
S A N G R I L Y D E P R I V
P B A B E C P D F W A I M G
A U A I E I E K A L R Z M Z
R S G S D R B L S D I Z G I
K I U V I P B W B L M L A L
L L G R L B L A Z I L Y T U
Y Y H M Y Z Y C R A C K L Y
```

Name _____

Whistler's mother, Anna McNeill Whistler, may be one of the most

_____ _____ in
(recognize + able) (lady + es)

history because of the portrait her son

_____ painted. James Whistler often
(able + ly)

_____ with his
(disagree + ed)

_____ strict mother. Yet he
(extreme + ly)

greatly _____ her sympathetic
(admire + ed)

_____ and praised her
(quality + es)

_____ to others. For
(kindhearted + ness)

example, Anna Whistler _____ herself
(devote + ed)

to _____ twenty bedridden people
(nurse + ing)

before they died. James Whistler's feelings

were also _____ by his mother's face.
(stir + ed)

In her face, he saw "grace _____ to
(wed + ed)

dignity, strength _____
(enhance + ing)

sweetness."

Whistler _____ to paint his
(decide + ed)

mother's portrait when she was sixty-five.

She _____ in a black dress and
(pose + ed)

_____ bonnet. She was
(white-lace + ed)

_____ to be _____
(require + ed)   (motion + less)

for long hours while her son _____
(busy + ly)

painted. Though the portrait is now

famous, there were no _____ for it, at
(buy + ers)

first. _____ , Whistler sold it to a
(Final + ly)

museum for $625. Today it is a

_____ work of art.
(price + less)

1. _____ Have many people seen the portrait of Whistler's mother?

2. _____ Did James Whistler almost always agree with his mother?

3. _____ Did James think his mother was a kind woman?

4. _____ Did James see prettiness and girlishness in his mother's face?

5. _____ Did the bonnet in the portrait have white lace?

Definition An **outline** can help you summarize an article for study. A **topic outline** uses nouns and short phrases to state the main ideas.

James Whistler is considered one of the best American artists of the 1800s. He was born in 1834 in Massachusetts. When he was nine, he moved with his family to Russia. Later his family moved back to the United States, and Whistler studied art in the East. At the age of twenty-two, he moved to France and seriously devoted himself to art. London, England, became his permanent home after 1859.

Whistler created many paintings, etchings, and lithographs. His most famous painting, commonly known as Whistler's Mother, is titled *Arrangement in Black and Gray.* Other important works are *The White Girl, Self Portrait, The Ocean,* and *Nocturne in Black and Gold.*

Arrangement in Black and Gray

1. In what places did Whistler make his **residence?**

_____ _____ _____

_____ _____

2. What were some of Whistler's most famous **paintings?**

_____ _____

_____ _____

► **Directions**

Complete the outline. Use the words in boldface print above to help you write the headings. Then use the answers to the questions to help write the topics, or main facts.

James Whistler

I. _____   II. _____

   A. _____   A. _____

   B. _____   B. _____

   C. _____   C. _____

   D. _____   D. _____

   E. _____   E. _____

Name _____

Rules If a word ends in **f** or **fe**, usually change the **f** or **fe** to **v** and add **es** to make the word plural. Exceptions to this rule are *chief, belief, reef,* and *roof.* A word that ends in **ff** is made plural by adding **s.**

wolf—wol**ves**   knife—kni**ves**
cliff—cli**ffs**   chief—chie**fs**

1. puff _____
2. elf _____
3. cuff _____

4. hoof _____
5. thief _____
6. knife _____

7. muff _____
8. wolf _____
9. calf _____

10. scarf _____
11. roof _____
12. reef _____

13. sniff _____
14. cliff _____
15. staff _____

16. chief _____
17. sheaf _____
18. life _____

▶ **Directions**

For each clue or definition below, write the correct plural word.

19. _____ horses' feet

20. _____ baby cattle

21. _____ cutting instruments

22. _____ heads of tribes

23. _____ what your nose does

24. _____ tops of houses

25. _____ wild animals, similar to dogs

26. _____ outlaws who steal

27. _____ bands around the wrists

28. _____ tiny imaginary folk

29. _____ cloths worn on the head or neck

30. _____ ridges of rocks in an ocean or lake, often made of coral

31. _____ steep sides of rocks

32. _____ short bursts of smoke or steam

33. _____ sticks or poles used for support when walking

1.
_____

2.
_____

3.
_____

4.
_____

5.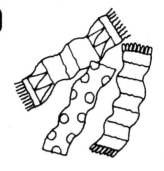
_____

6.
_____

7.
_____

8.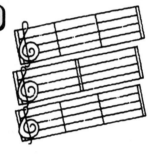
_____

9.
_____

10.
_____

11.
_____

12.
_____

Name _____

 Directions

Form the plural of each word by adding **s** or **es**.

Rule If a word ends in **o**, an **s** is usually added to make the word plural. For some exceptions, the plural is formed by adding **es**.

potato—potatoes	echo—echoes
buffalo—buffaloes	hero—heroes
torpedo—torpedoes	tornado—tornadoes

1. stereo_____
2. hero_____
3. photo_____
4. rodeo_____

5. avocado_____
6. piccolo_____
7. piano_____
8. tuxedo_____

9. solo_____
10. tempo_____
11. poncho_____
12. tomato_____

13. domino_____
14. burro_____
15. radio_____
16. kangaroo_____

 Directions

Write a plural word from above to complete each sentence.

17. At the outdoor cafe, Maria and Tina ordered tuna salad with juicy red

_____ .

18. It was chilly out, so they were glad they had worn their _____ .

19. Maria had brought her camera and hoped to get some _____ of the concert.

20. They had listened to the musicians on their _____ but had never seen them.

21. They arrived just as two men in black _____ came on stage.

22. The men sat at _____ and played several duets.

23. Then they took turns playing _____ .

24. Later they were joined by a quartet of flutes and _____ .

25. Tina enjoyed the ballads, but Maria liked the songs with livelier _____ .

Lesson 70: Plural form for words ending in O

139

▶ Directions

The plural forms of the words in the box will help you answer the questions. Use the plural words to complete the crossword puzzle.

photo	soprano
rodeo	solo
piano	tornado
potato	tomato
avocado	sombrero
kangaroo	torpedo

Across

1. What are red and juicy and used in making spaghetti sauce?
3. What are hopping animals found in Australia?
7. What can a photographer take?
9. What does Kansas have more of than any other state?
10. What are pieces of music for one voice or one instrument called?
11. In what kinds of contests do contestants ride horses bareback for 10 seconds?

Down

2. What are cigar-shaped missiles used under water called?
4. What do you call broad-brimmed hats that tie under the chin?
5. What are pear-shaped fruits with large pits in the middle?
6. Who are people with the highest singing voices?
7. Which vegetables taste good baked, mashed, French fried, or scalloped?
8. For which instruments did Mozart and Chopin write music?

Lesson 70: Plural form for words ending in O

Name _____

The words in the box are the same in their singular and plural forms. Choose one of the words to complete each pair of sentences.

Rule Some words do not change at all in their plural form.

sauerkraut	aircraft	spinach	spaghetti	oatmeal
salmon	chili	broccoli	trout	zucchini
scissors	series	moose	shrimp	wheat

1. A small, two-engine _____ just landed.

   Three jet _____ took off within the last ten minutes.

2. The _____ had large antlers.

   The herd of _____ was headed toward the lake.

3. She picked a _____ from the garden.

   The recipe called for three _____ .

Directions

Complete each phrase by writing the plural of the word in parentheses. You may use your dictionary.

Rule A few words change completely in their plural form. Other plural forms may not be familiar because they come from other languages.

tooth—teeth   crisis—crises
ox—oxen   phenomenon—phenomena

4. six wild _____
   (goose)

5. three lovely _____
   (woman)

6. four watery _____
   (oasis)

7. five generous _____
   (alumnus)

8. six tiny _____
   (mouse)

9. two dangerous _____
   (bacterium)

10. two tired _____
    (foot)

11. six annoying _____
    (louse)

12. five handsome _____
    (man)

13. eight noisy _____
    (child)

Complete the sentences with the plural forms of the words in parentheses.

1. The Smiths and the Carters were going to the college's _____ picnic.
   (alumnus)

2. That morning, the Carters' daughter lost two loose _____ .
   (tooth)

3. Mrs. Smith saw two _____ in her basement while getting the picnic basket.
   (mouse)

4. Despite these _____ , both families were ready to leave on schedule.
   (crisis)

5. The picnic ground was near the woods, and they saw some _____ .
   (deer)

6. There was a lake nearby with more _____ than they had ever seen.
   (goose)

7. The _____ had made sandwiches and brought _____ for
   (woman)   (popcorn)
   snacks.

8. Their husbands had made a salad of _____ , _____ , and
   (spinach)   (zucchini)
   tomatoes.

9. After lunch, the _____ decided to take advantage of the fishing.
   (man)

10. They had fished for _____ but had never fished for _____
    (salmon)   (trout)
    before.

11. The _____ hiked through the woods until their _____ hurt.
    (child)   (foot)

12. They were sure they had spotted two _____ with big antlers.
    (moose)

13. They were told that they probably had seen _____ .
    (elk)

14. The highlight was scenic flights over the lake in two _____ .
    (aircraft)

Name _____

 Directions

Write a word from the box to complete each sentence. Then list each word under
the correct heading.

apologized	misunderstanding	disagreements	unfairly	appreciated
endangered	unfortunately	sympathetic	unpleasant	understood

1. Sometimes friends have serious _____.

2. _____, it happened to John and Carl.

3. For two days, there were _____ feelings between them.

4. Then John realized that he had treated Carl _____.

5. He knew he had _____ their friendship.

6. He wanted to clear up the _____.

7. He _____ to Carl for misjudging him.

8. Carl _____ how John could have made the mistake.

9. John _____ Carl's understanding.

10. It was good to have a friend who was so _____.

Three syllables

_____   _____

_____   _____

Four syllables

_____

_____

_____

Five syllables

_____

_____

_____

▶ **Directions**

Find the word in each pair that ends in **le** or is a compound word, and divide it into syllables, using vertical lines. Write **S** on the line if the words are synonyms, or mean the same. Write **A** if they are antonyms, or have opposite meanings.

Rule Divide a compound word between the words that make the compound word.

tea/pot   like/wise
never/the/less

Rule When a word ends in **le** preceded by a consonant, divide the word before that consonant.

a/ble   bea/gle
tin/gle

1. giggle/laugh _____
2. tumble/fall _____
3. park/playground _____
4. snapshot/photo _____
5. handbag/purse _____
6. stifle/stop _____
7. shake/tremble _____
8. worthwhile/useless _____
9. fable/story _____
10. sweetheart/enemy _____
11. lowly/noble _____
12. glitter/sparkle _____
13. strong/feeble _____
14. chew/nibble _____
15. uncle/aunt _____
16. unfit/able _____
17. hardship/ease _____
18. battle/fight _____
19. arouse/kindle _____
20. gigantic/little _____
21. forever/enduring _____
22. breakdown/collapse _____
23. grasslands/plains _____
24. proud/humble _____
25. pebble/stone _____
26. foolproof/complex _____
27. nimble/spry _____
28. agree/quibble _____
29. into/out _____
30. stable/disrupted _____
31. cottontail/rabbit _____
32. gentle/harsh _____
33. smooth/wrinkle _____

Name _____

 Directions

Study the rules. Then read each sentence. On the lines next to each sentence, divide the two words in boldface print into syllables, using vertical lines.

Rule When two or more consonants come between two vowels, the word is usually divided between the first two consonants.
    bet/ter   pic/ture

Rule When a single consonant comes between two vowels, the word is usually divided after the consonant if the first vowel is short.
    clev/er   rob/in

Rule When a single consonant comes between two vowels, the word is usually divided before the consonant if the first vowel is long.
    ma/jor   pri/vate

1. It was a **sunny** day for a **picnic.**   _____   _____

2. A group of friends went to the park that was **beyond** the **forest.**   _____   _____

3. Jack had **never** been there **before.**   _____   _____

4. Jane said to **follow** her through the **tunnel.**   _____   _____

5. Maria and Adam brought their **tennis racquets.**   _____   _____

6. Jane spread out the **yellow blanket.**   _____   _____

7. Adam was **hungry** and opened the **basket.**   _____   _____

8. He took out the **napkins** and **paper** plates.   _____   _____

9. They had cheese sandwiches with **lettuce** and **olives.**   _____   _____

10. For dessert they ate some **melon** that had a very sweet **flavor.**   _____   _____

Directions

Write the number of syllables you hear in each word. Then write the word and use vertical lines to divide it into syllables.

Rule When a compound word has more than two syllables, first divide between the words that make up the compound word. Then divide the smaller words into syllables.

flow/er/pot
ev/er/y/bod/y

Rule When a word has more than two syllables, figure out how many syllables it has. Then divide it into syllables according to the rules you have learned.

pro/nun/ci/a/tion
sub/ur/ban

1. expertly _____ _____

2. expression _____ _____

3. disbelief _____ _____

4. inefficient _____ _____

5. determination _____ _____

6. kangaroos _____ _____

7. strawberries _____ _____

8. shopkeeper _____ _____

9. inseparable _____ _____

10. quickened _____ _____

11. illegal _____ _____

12. drizzled _____ _____

13. distribution _____ _____

14. corporation _____ _____

15. windowpane _____ _____

16. scorekeeper _____ _____

17. igloos _____ _____

18. shredding _____ _____

19. operations _____ _____

20. irreversible _____ _____

21. football _____ _____

22. decided _____ _____

23. gratefully _____ _____

24. abilities _____ _____

25. battery _____ _____

26. geographical _____ _____

27. proceeded _____ _____

28. congratulations _____ _____

29. improper _____ _____

30. idea _____ _____

31. showboat _____ _____

32. puppeteer _____ _____

33. repetition _____ _____

34. oneself _____ _____

35. windowpane _____ _____

36. fingerprint _____ _____

Name _____

► **Directions**

Read the article. Complete each unfinished sentence by writing the plural form of each word on the line above it.

Since the early _____ of the colonies, _____ ,
                 (day)   (man)

_____ , and _____ have enjoyed local fairs. City and county
    (woman)   (child)

fairs are a high point in people's _____ because they offer fun and
                                  (life)

entertainment for everyone. Many people take part in _____ and weightlifting.
                                            (rodeo)

There are _____ for the children to ride. Men and women enjoy
                (pony)

demonstrations of new ways of cooking vegetables such as _____ ,
                                             (spinach)

_____ , _____ , and _____ .
   (broccoli)   (zucchini)   (potato)

    The booths were the highlight of one county fair. Some of the booths were for fun and games, while others were for information. For example, one booth offered a free pamphlet

about the effects of food on skin, hair, and _____ . Another booth featured a
                                           (tooth)

display called "Hometown _____ ." "Some Strange _____ and
                        (Hero)   (Belief)

Customs of Our Ancestors" was another popular attraction. By looking at this display, people

learned that _____ were once thought to be poisonous. They were called
              (tomato)

"peaches of _____ ."
           (wolf)

Definition Remember, an **outline** helps you summarize the important ideas in a story or article. A **topic outline** is written with words or short phrases that state the main ideas.

Potatoes are an ancient food. Indians in South America began growing them centuries before Europeans discovered the continent. These delicious vegetables provide us with vitamin C, iron, and protein. Many people think they are fattening, but potatoes are actually low in calories. It's what you put on them—butter or sour cream—that adds the calories!

Tomatoes also originated in South America. They are an excellent source of vitamins A and C. Tomatoes are used in countless dishes. You will find them in salads, pizza and spaghetti sauces, stews, and soups.

1. What vegetable is the first paragraph about? _____

2. Where were they grown long ago? _____

3. What nutrients do they provide? _____

4. What food is the second paragraph about? _____

5. Where did they originate? _____

6. What nutrients do they provide? _____

Directions

Now use your answers to complete the outline below.

Two Terrific Vegetables

First Heading   I. _____

     A. _____

     B. _____

Second Heading   II. _____

     A. _____

     B. _____

Name _____

▶ **Directions**

Read the words in each group and write them in alphabetical order.

1. tiger   table   today
that   teach

_____

_____

_____

_____

_____

2. circle   cabin   claim
chalk   ceiling

_____

_____

_____

_____

_____

3. indeed   illusion   imagine
imitate   inflate

_____

_____

_____

_____

_____

4. habit   hadn't   hammer
hall   hair

_____

_____

_____

_____

_____

5. paddle   panel   painter
palace   pants

_____

_____

_____

_____

_____

6. rear   realize   realist
ready   realm

_____

_____

_____

_____

_____

▶ **Directions**

Number the words in each group to show the correct alphabetical order.

7. bungalow   _____

bundle   _____

bunt   _____

bunk   _____

bunch   _____

8. locker   _____

locality   _____

locket   _____

locomotive   _____

locate   _____

Directions

Read the guide words and entry words in each column. Circle any entry words that would *not* be on the same page as those guide words. Then number the rest of the words in the column in alphabetical order.

Hint In the dictionary, the **guide words** at the top of the page show the first and last entries on the page. All the other entries on that page are in alphabetical order between those words.

1. ascend/auditorium

_____ attack

_____ asleep

_____ athlete

_____ astonish

_____ artist

2. macaroni/make

manager _____

machinery _____

made _____

majestic _____

magnify _____

3. swallow/swung

swoop _____

switch _____

symphony _____

swam _____

survey _____

 Directions

Find four words in the box that would be on the dictionary page with each pair of guide words. Write those words in alphabetical order below the guide words.

| coal | level | limp | coast | coin | dark | dance |
| decide | date | clump | cocoa | dahlia | lift | liberty |

4. club/coil

_____

_____

_____

_____

5. daily/deep

_____

_____

_____

_____

6. lesson/listen

_____

_____

_____

_____

Name _____

 Directions

Study the pronunciation key. Then look at the words in the box and read and say each symbol below the box. Write the word from the box that has the sound that symbol stands for. The key words in the pronunciation key will help you.

Hint The dictionary respelling beside each entry word helps you pronounce that word. The dictionary's pronunciation key shows the symbols used in the respelling.

Vowels				Consonants			
Symbol	**Key Words**	**Symbol**	**Key Words**	**Symbol**	**Key Words**	**Symbol**	**Key Words**
a	cat	u	up	b	bed	ch	chin, arch
ā	ape	ʉ	fur, shirt	d	dog	ŋ	ring, drink
ä	cot, car			f	fall	sh	she, push
		ə	= a in ago	g	get	th	thin, truth
e	ten, berry		e in agent	h	help	*th*	then, father
ē	me		i in pencil	j	jump	zh	measure
			o in atom	k	kiss, call		
i	fit, here		u in circus	l	leg		
ī	ice, fire			m	meat		
				n	nose		
ō	go			p	put		
ô	fall, for			r	red		
oi	oil			s	see		
၀၀	look, pull			t	top		
o͞o	tool, rule			v	vat		
ou	out, crowd			w	wish		
				y	yard		
				z	zebra		

spurt	spoil	sting	school	those	people
thrift	should	treasure	pail	gallop	chart

1. g _____   **2.** o͞o _____

3. ā _____   **4.** th _____

5. zh _____   **6.** ē _____

7. oi _____   **8.** sh _____

9. ŋ _____   **10.** *th* _____

11. ä _____   **12.** ʉ _____

► **Directions**

Use the pronunciation key and accent marks to help you say each respelled word. Then read the word that goes with the respelling. Circle the letter or letters in each word that stand for the schwa sound.

Rule When words have two or more syllables, some syllables are stressed, or accented, more than others. A heavy accent mark (´) in the dictionary respelling shows which syllable receives the primary, or heavier, accent. A lighter accent mark (´) shows a secondary, or lesser, accent. The vowel sound often heard in unaccented syllables is usually represented in dictionaries by the schwa symbol (ə).

1. ə plôd´   a p p l a u d
2. nes´ ə ser´ ē   n e c e s s a r y
3. sul´ fər   s u l f u r
4. jen´ ər ə le   g e n e r a l l y
5. im bal´ əns   i m b a l a n c e
6. kən sʉrn´   c o n c e r n
7. en sī´ klə pē´ dē ə   e n c y c l o p e d i a
8. sim plis´ ə tē   s i m p l i c i t y
9. ed´ it ər   e d i t o r
10. mōt´ ər bōt   m o t o r b o a t

► **Directions**

Use the pronunciation key and accent marks to help you say each respelled word below. In front of each respelling, write the word from the box that is represented by the respelling.

11. _____ ek´ sər sīz

12. _____ ə fish´ ē āt

13. _____ kʉr´ ən sē

14. _____ mis´ un dər stand´

15. _____ prē zən tā´ shən

16. _____ meg´ ə fōn

17. _____ ə fek´ tiv

18. _____ plen´ ti fəl

19. _____ ker´ ə sēn

misunderstand
effective
officiate
megaphone
exercise
presentation
currency
plentiful
kerosene

Name _____

a	cat	ō	go	ʉ	fur	ə = a in ago
ā	ape	ô	fall, for	ch	chin	e in agent
ä	cot, car	oo	look	sh	she	i in pencil
e	ten	o͞o	tool	th	thin	o in atom
ē	me	oi	oil	*th*	then	u in circus
i	fit	ou	out	zh	measure	
ī	ice	u	up	ŋ	ring	

▶ Directions

Read each sentence. Use the pronunciation key and accent marks to pronounce the respelled word in the sentence. Then fill in the circle beside the word that is represented by the respelling.

1. Scientists believe that the earliest (in hab´ i tənts) of China lived in caves.
   ○ inhibitions   ○ inhabitants   ○ inheritance

2. Later, scientists think, these people began to farm and keep (dō mes´ tik) animals.
   ○ domestic   ○ domesticated   ○ domicile

3. Several ancient settlements have been (di skuv´ ərd) in China.
   ○ disclosed   ○ discovered   ○ discouraged

4. Scientists have (eg zam´ ind) the ruins of these settlements.
   ○ examined   ○ examination   ○ excavated

5. Some of the oldest of these settlements are located in the rich (val´ ē) of the Hwang Ho River.
   ○ valid   ○ valley   ○ value

6. These settlements, say the scientists, were (kən struk´ tid) as long ago as 2000 B.C.
   ○ erected   ○ construction   ○ constructed

7. The people of these settlements developed a form of strong (guv´ ərn mənt).
   ○ governor   ○ government   ○ governing

8. They also were able to make (bränz) tools.
   ○ bronze   ○ bronzed   ○ brass

9. In time, the settlements were united into city-states and (em´ pīrz).
   ○ umpires   ○ employs   ○ empires

Directions

Read each word. Beside it, write the entry word you would look for in the dictionary.

1. striding _____

2. compliments _____

3. enraged _____

4. guiltily _____

5. resistance _____

6. geese _____

7. connected _____

8. driving _____

9. sang _____

10. jetties _____

Directions

Read the paragraphs. Notice the numbered words in boldface print. Write each numbered word as you would find it as a dictionary entry word.

Mongolia is **located** east of the Chinese
                11
province of Sinkiang. Within Mongolia is the
Gobi Desert, one of the **largest** desert areas
                                    12
in the world. Large plains, or **steppes,** where
                                    13
most of the population live, surround the
Gobi. For **centuries,** the people of Mongolia
           14
have **kept** herds of livestock on these
        15
steppes.

   Present-day Mongolians live mostly by
tending the herds. Their **ancestors,** the
                              16

Mongols, were among the **world's** most
                                   17
feared warriors. In the 1100s and 1200s,
  18
their leader, Genghis Khan, and his
successors led these warriors on military
   19   20
conquests that reached from Europe to
  21
Southeast Asia to the Middle East. In fact,
the famous Great Wall of China was **built** in
                                          22
an unsuccessful attempt to keep the Mongol
warriors out of China.

11. _____   15. _____   19. _____

12. _____   16. _____   20. _____

13. _____   17. _____   21. _____

14. _____   18. _____   22. _____

Name _____

▶ **Directions**

Read the article, and notice the words in boldface print.
Then read the dictionary entries for each of those words,
and underline the definition that fits the article.

Rule In the dictionary, when there is more than one meaning for an entry word, numbers identify the different definitions. The meaning listed first is usually the most commonly used.

Lima is Peru's largest city. It has almost one-fourth of the country's population. It also is Peru's economic and administrative **capital.** Most of the manufactured **goods** produced in Peru are made in Lima and other cities along the coast. The nearby **port** of Callao contributes with its fisheries and petroleum refineries.

Unlike many other cities, Lima did not simply happen by **accident.** It was founded in 1535 by Francisco Pizarro. After conquering the Inca inhabitants of Peru, Pizarro looked for a place that would be in the **center** of the lands he had captured for the Spanish empire. He decided against using the Inca royal city of Cusco. Instead he ordered the **construction** of a new city nearer to the sea and more convenient for land transportation.

Pizarro's city became known as the City of Kings. It was famous for its carefully planned center. Its orderly system of streets and the careful arrangement of its official **buildings** made it a showplace among the cities of Spain's American empire. Today the City of Kings is called Lima.

accident (ak´ si dənt) *n.* **1** a happening that is not expected or planned **2** an unfortunate happening or instance of bad luck that causes damage or injury **3** chance

building (bil´ diŋ) *n.* **1** anything that is built with walls and a roof; a structure, such as a house, factory, or school **2** the act or work of one who builds

capital (kap´ it'l) *n.* **1** *the same as* CAPITAL LETTER **2** a city where the government of a state or nation is located **3** money or property that is put into a business or that is used to make more money

center (sen´ tər) *n.* **1** a point inside a circle or sphere that is the same distance from all points on the circumference or surface **2** the middle point or part; the place at the middle **3** a person whose position is at the middle point

construction (kən struk´ shən) *n.* **1** the act of constructing or building **2** the way in which something is constructed or put together **3** the arrangement of words in a sentence

goods (goodz) *pl.n.* **1** things made to be sold; wares **2** personal property that can be moved

port (pôrt) *n.* **1** a harbor **2** a city with a harbor where ships can load and unload

▶ **Directions**

Read these entries. Decide which word to use to complete each sentence below. Write the word and its number on the line in the sentence. You may need to add a suffix to the entry word.

Rule An entry word may be followed by a raised number. This tells you that there is another word spelled the same way that has a different meaning or origin.

close¹ (klōs) *adj.* stuffy and full of stale air
close² (klōz) *v.* to make no longer open; shut
desert¹ (də zʉrt´) *v.* to go away from someone or something that one ought not to leave
desert² (dez´ ərt) *n.* a dry, sandy region with little or no plant life

elder¹ (el´dər) *adj.* older
elder² (el´dər) *n.* a shrub or tree with small, white flowers and red or purple berries
prune¹ (pro͞on) *n.* a plum dried for eating
prune² (pro͞on) *v.* to cut or trim branches, twigs, etc. from

1. My _____ sister Kara visited me last Saturday.

2. When she arrived, I was _____ the bushes.

3. "I'm spring cleaning; don't _____ me," I teased.

4. "I'll trim this overgrown _____," Kara replied.

5. When we cleaned the attic, it felt very _____.

6. Someone had _____ the window, and it had jammed.

7. After our chores, Kara and I snacked on _____.

Name _____

 Directions

Practice your dictionary skills. Read these entries, then do what each sentence tells you to do.

advanced [ad vanst´] *adj.* **1** far on in life; old **2** ahead of the times or of other people
architecture [är´ kə tek´ chər] *n.* **1** the science or work of planning and putting up buildings **2** a style or special way of building
arrive [ə rīv´] *v.* to come to a place after a journey
calendar [kal´ ən dər] *n.* **1** a system for arranging time into days, weeks, months, and years **2** a table or chart showing such an arrangement, usually for a single year

civilization [siv´ ə li zā´ shən] *n.* **1** the stage in the progress of human beings when they have developed a written language, arts, sciences, government, etc. **2** the way of life of a people, nation, or period
conquer [käŋ´ kər] *v.* to get or gain by using force, such as by winning a war
develop [dē vel´ əp] *v.* **1** to make or become larger, fuller, better **2** to bring or come into being and work out gradually; evolve **3** to become known

1. Circle any entry word below that would not be on the same dictionary page as the guide words **adamant/arduous.**

arrive   architecture   advanced

2. List each entry word that has two syllables.

_____

3. Write the entry word that rhymes with *danced.*

_____

4. Write each entry word that has a secondary accent mark.

_____

5. Write the entry word whose first syllable has the same vowel sound as the word *bark.*

_____

 Directions

Write the number of the meaning of the word in boldface print that is used in each sentence below.

_____ **6.** Ancient Egypt was a **civilization** that flourished over 5,000 years ago.

_____ **7.** The Egyptians were very **advanced** in medicine and astronomy.

_____ **8.** They devised a 365-day **calendar** based on the movement of the sun.

_____ **9.** They **developed** picture writing into a complicated system of symbols.

_____ **10.** The Great Pyramid is a well-known example of Egyptian **architecture.**

▶ Directions

Suppose you have just finished writing the report below. Proofread the paragraphs. Correct each error in spelling or in the endings added to words. Circle each error and write the correction above it. The dictionary entries on page 157 will help you.

Hint It's a good idea to proofread what you have written. Use the dictionary to check for spelling errors and to make sure that you are using words correctly.

According to modern scientists, two of the most important early Latin American civilizatins were the Mayan and the Aztec. Mayan civilition was developed on the Yucatán Peninsula and the lowlands of Guatemala. Beginning around the first century and develeping rapidly, Mayan civlisation reached its peak from A.D. 200 to 800. The Mayan Indians were skilled astronomers, with an advanceed and highly accurate calendar that is still admired today. Creating remarkable art and arcitescshur the Maya were also the first Indians in America to create an advanst system of writing.

The Aztec Indians developed their civalizashun to the north of the Maya, in the Valley of Mexico. Their civilization came toward the end of the long period of development of the Central American Indains and included large cities and a well-organized government that ruled large populations. When the Spanish conkeror Cortes arriveed in Mexico in the 1500s, he found a highly advanst Aztec culture.

- **Analogy:** Tells the relationship that one thing has to another. (kitten is to cat as puppy is to dog)

- **Antonyms:** Words that have opposite or almost opposite meanings.

- **Apostrophe:** This mark (') is an apostrophe. An apostrophe can be added to a word to show possession—that someone or something owns or has something. (Ellen's book) An apostrophe can also be used to stand for the missing letters in a contraction. (isn't = is not)

- **Base Word:** A word to which a prefix or suffix may be added to form a new word. (**print**er, un**pack**, **like**ly)

- **Compound Word:** A word that is made up of two smaller words. Each small word can stand alone and still have meaning. (dog + house = **doghouse**)

- **Consonant(s):** The letters of the alphabet except **a, e, i, o,** and **u.** The letters **w** and **y** can be either consonants or vowels depending on their sound in a word.

- **Consonant Blend:** In a consonant blend, two or more consonants are sounded together so that each consonant can be heard. (**bl**ack, **tr**ain, **spr**ing, fa**st,** la**mp**)

- **Consonant Digraph:** In a consonant digraph, two consonants are sounded together to make one sound. (**wh**en, **th**in, **ch**in, **sh**eep, clo**th**, pa**ck**)

- **Contraction:** A short way to write two words. The two words are written together, leaving out one or more letters. An apostrophe stands for the missing letters.

- **Diphthong:** In a diphthong, two letters are blended together to make one vowel sound. (cl**ou**d, b**oy**, **oi**l, c**ow**, n**ew**)

- **Homographs:** Words that are spelled the same, but have different meanings and different word backgrounds. Some homographs have different pronunciations.

- **Homonyms:** Words that sound alike but have different meanings. They may or may not have different spellings.

- **Main Idea:** A main idea sentence tells what a paragraph is about.

- **Prefix:** A word part that is added at the beginning of a base or root word to change the word's meaning or form a new word. (**re**cycle, **un**wrap, **dis**appear)

- **Root:** A word part to which a prefix or suffix may be added to form a new word. (intro**duct**ion, pro**spect**or, re**duce**)

- **Suffix:** A word part that is added at the end of a root or base word to change the word's meaning or the way it is used. (sprint**er**, dark**ness**, help**ful**)

- **Syllable:** A word or word part with a single vowel sound.

- **Synonym(s):** Words that have the same or almost the same meaning.

- **Vowel(s):** The letters **a, i, u o,** and **e.** The letters **y** and **w** can also be vowels when **y** has the long **i** or long **e** sound and when **w** is part of a vowel digraph, as in p**aw,** or diphthong, as in c**ow.**

- **Vowel Digraph:** In a vowel digraph, two vowels together can make a long or short sound or have a special sound all of their own. Vowel digraphs don't follow the long vowel rules. [br**ea**k (ĭ), h**ea**d (ĕ)]

- **Vowel Pair:** In a vowel pair, two vowels come together to make one long vowel sound. The first vowel stands for the long sound, and the second vowel is silent. [**ai**m (ĭ), pl**ay** (ĭ)]

▶ General Rules

- **Short-Vowel Rule:** If a word or syllable has only one vowel and it comes at the beginning or between two consonants, the vowel is usually short. (**a**m, **i**s, b**a**g, f**o**x)

- **Long-Vowel Rule I:** If a syllable has two vowels, the first vowel is usually long and the second vowel is silent. (r**ai**n, k**i**t**e**, c**a**n**e**, j**ee**p, r**ay**)

- **Long-Vowel Rule II:** If a word or syllable has one vowel and it comes at the end of the word or syllable, the vowel is usually long. (w**e**, g**o**, p**o**ny)

- **Y as a Vowel Rule:**
  1) If **y** is the only vowel at the end of a one-syllable word, **y** has the sound of **long i**. (fl**y**, b**y**)
  2) If **y** is the only vowel at the end of a word of more than one syllable, **y** usually has the sound of **long e**. (sill**y**, bab**y**)

- **Soft C and G Rule:** When **c** or **g** is followed by **e, i,** or **y**, it is usually soft. (i**c**e, **c**ity, chan**g**e, **g**ym)

- **To make a word plural:**
  1) Usually just add **s**. (cat**s**, dog**s**, kite**s**)
  2) If a word ends in **x, z, ss, sh,** or **ch,** usually add **es**. (fox**es**, dress**es**, peach**es**)
  3) If a word ends in **y** preceded by a consonant, change the **y** to **i** and add **es**. (fl**ies**, fair**ies**, bab**ies**)
  4) If a word ends in **f** or **fe,** usually change the **f** or **fe** to **v** and add **es**. (wolf/wol**ves**, knife/kni**ves**)
  5) If a word ends in **o,** usually just add **s** to make the word plural. Some words are made plural by adding **es**. (potato/potato**es**, tomato/tomato**es**, hero/hero**es**)
  6) Some words change their vowel sound in the plural form. (man/**men**, tooth/**teeth**, mouse/**mice**)

- **To add other suffixes:**
  1) When a short-vowel word ends in a single consonant, usually double the consonant before adding a suffix that begins with a vowel. (ru**nn**ing, hu**mm**ed, ba**tt**er)
  2) When a word ends in silent **e,** drop the **e** before adding a suffix that begins with a vowel. (bak**ing**, tap**ed**, lat**est**)
  3) When a word ends in **y** preceded by a consonant, change the **y** to **i** before adding a suffix other than **ing**. (cr**ied**, happ**ily**, funn**ier**, pon**ies**) For the suffix **ing** do not change the **y** to **i**. (cry**ing**, try**ing**)

- **To make a noun show possession:**
  1) Add **'s** to a singular noun. (dog**'s**, Bob**'s**, child**'s**)
  2) Add an apostrophe only to a plural noun that ends in **s**. (boys**'**, the Browns**'**, babies**'**)
  3) Add **'s** to a plural noun that does not end in **s**. (mice**'s**, children**'s**, women**'s**)